Houghton Mifflin Math

Practice Activities

Authors

Lelon R. Capps
University of Kansas
Lawrence, Kansas

W. G. Quast
Slippery Rock University
Slippery Rock, Pennsylvania

Mary Ann Haubner
Mount Saint Joseph College
Cincinnati, Ohio

William L. Cole
Michigan State University
East Lansing, Michigan

Leland Webb
California State College
Bakersfield, California

Charles E. Allen
Los Angeles Unified
  School District
Los Angeles, California

Coordinating Author

Ernest R. Duncan
Professor Emeritus
Rutgers University
New Brunswick, New Jersey

Houghton Mifflin Company   BOSTON

Atlanta   Dallas   Geneva, Ill.   Lawrenceville, N.J.   Palo Alto   Toronto

Credits

Cover photography by Lehman Millet Incorporated
Text design by Ligature, Inc.
Art and Production by Ligature, Inc.

Illustration

Ruth Roman Brunke   2, 15, 17, 20, 34, 67, 88, 104,
    115, 120
Rondi Collette   29, 33, 40, 44, 50, 64, 70, 89, 99, 102,
    118, 127, 138, 142
Shelley Dieterichs   28, 39, 43, 46, 73, 85, 100, 117, 128
Creston Ely   30, 37, 42, 51, 55, 61, 66, 69, 71, 76, 91, 92,
    119
Judith Friedman   32, 38, 41, 45, 48, 62, 63, 68, 72, 90,
    107, 108, 114
Walter Gaffney-Kessel   47
Richard Lo   6, 24, 25, 35, 53, 56, 65, 74, 75, 84, 94, 101,
    112, 116, 125, 135, 136, 143
Gary Matusek   12, 18, 23
Jeff O'Connor   10, 13, 21

Contents

The Commutative Property of Addition

Changing the order of the addends does not change the sum.

$$2 + 3 = 5$$
$$3 + 2 = 5$$

The Opposites Property of Addition

Subtraction undoes addition.

$$2 + 3 = 5$$
$$5 - 3 = 2$$

The Zero Property of Addition

The sum of zero and any number is that number.

$$3 + 0 = 3$$
$$0 + 2 = 2$$

The Zero Property of Subtraction

The difference between any number and zero is that number.

$$8 - 0 = 8$$

The difference between any number and itself is zero.

$$6 - 6 = 0$$

Use the commutative property to complete.

1. $5 + 4 = \underline{\quad} + 5$ **2.** $7 + 9 = \underline{\quad} + 7$ **3.** $4 + 1 = \underline{\quad} + 4$

4. $7 + 3 = 3 + \underline{\quad}$ **5.** $8 + 6 = 6 + \underline{\quad}$ **6.** $9 + 2 = 2 + \underline{\quad}$

7. $4 + 9 = 9 + \underline{\quad}$ **8.** $4 + 11 = \underline{\quad} + 4$ **9.** $7 + 6 = \underline{\quad} + 7$

Use the zero property to complete.

10. $9 - 0 = \underline{\quad}$ **11.** $0 + 1 = \underline{\quad}$ **12.** $0 + 8 = \underline{\quad}$

13. $12 + 0 = \underline{\quad}$ **14.** $15 - 0 = \underline{\quad}$ **15.** $2 - 2 = \underline{\quad}$

Use the opposites property to complete.

16. $8 + 4 = 12$, so $12 - 4 = \underline{\quad}$ **17.** $10 - 6 = 4$, so $4 + 6 = \underline{\quad}$

18. $16 - 6 = 10$, so $10 + 6 = \underline{\quad}$ **19.** $9 + 3 = 12$, so $12 - 3 = \underline{\quad}$

Add or subtract.

20. $\begin{array}{r} 5 \\ +3 \\ \hline \end{array}$ **21.** $\begin{array}{r} 9 \\ -2 \\ \hline \end{array}$ **22.** $\begin{array}{r} 8 \\ -6 \\ \hline \end{array}$ **23.** $\begin{array}{r} 8 \\ +9 \\ \hline \end{array}$ **24.** $\begin{array}{r} 7 \\ +6 \\ \hline \end{array}$

25. $\begin{array}{r} 13 \\ -5 \\ \hline \end{array}$ **26.** $\begin{array}{r} 16 \\ -7 \\ \hline \end{array}$ **27.** $\begin{array}{r} 8 \\ -0 \\ \hline \end{array}$ **28.** $\begin{array}{r} 18 \\ -7 \\ \hline \end{array}$ **29.** $\begin{array}{r} 6 \\ +6 \\ \hline \end{array}$

30. $\begin{array}{r} 6 \\ +5 \\ \hline \end{array}$ **31.** $\begin{array}{r} 11 \\ -8 \\ \hline \end{array}$ **32.** $\begin{array}{r} 8 \\ +6 \\ \hline \end{array}$ **33.** $\begin{array}{r} 9 \\ -9 \\ \hline \end{array}$ **34.** $\begin{array}{r} 18 \\ -9 \\ \hline \end{array}$

1 PA

Practice
Student Book pp. 4–5

Add.

1.	6	2.	4	3.	7	4.	9	5.	8	6.	3
	4		6		3		5		3		2
	+5		+1		+8		+3		+2		+6

7.	2	8.	5	9.	7	10.	5	11.	1	12.	3
	7		4		5		1		8		9
	+3		+5		+8		+7		+9		+1

13.	7	14.	6	15.	8	16.	5	17.	3	18.	6
	3		2		4		2		9		8
	8		5		1		7		4		5
	+1		+4		+6		+8		+5		+9

19. $4 + 7 + 6 + 2 =$ _____

20. $7 + 5 + 1 + 5 =$ _____

21. $7 + 9 + 3 + 1 + 7 =$ _____

22. $2 + 8 + 4 + 4 + 6 =$ _____

23. $6 + 8 + 1 + 4 + 6 =$ _____

24. $5 + 6 + 7 + 4 + 7 =$ _____

25. $3 + 9 + 7 + 6 + 4 =$ _____

26. $5 + 7 + 4 + 3 + 8 =$ _____

Solve.

27. Jake's baseball team got 4 runs in the first inning, 2 runs in the second, and 3 runs in the fifth. How many runs did his team get in the three innings? _____

28. Mary's team scored 5 runs in one game, 7 runs in another game, and 8 runs in a third game. How many runs did her team score in a fourth game if the total number of runs scored was 23? _____

Name _____

Write the standard form for one thousand three hundred seven.

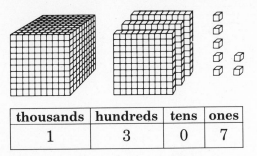

thousands	hundreds	tens	ones
1	3	0	7

GOVERNORS STATE UNIVERSITY
UNIVERSITY PARK
IL 60466

The standard form is 1307.

Write the number in standard form.

1. 3 thousands 8 hundreds 6 tens
5 ones

_____

2. 1 thousand 3 hundreds 2 tens
6 ones

_____

3. 6 hundreds 5 tens 6 ones

_____

4. 5 hundreds 7 tens

_____

5. 5 thousands 2 tens

_____

6. 1 hundred 1 one

_____

7. 2000 + 40 + 8

_____

8. 800 + 2

_____

9. 6000 + 3

_____

10. 1000 + 300

_____

Write the number in expanded form.

11. 368 _____   **12.** 906 _____   **13.** 4702 _____

Write the value of the underlined digit.

14. 8763 _____   **15.** 9526 _____   **16.** 4062 _____   **17.** 1439 _____

Write the standard form.

18. The jet traveled two thousand four kilometers. _____

19. The model train rode over six hundred twenty meters of
track. _____

20. Dina drove one thousand two hundred miles _____

21. There are three hundred two pages in the book. _____

3 PA

Practice

Write the standard form of 814 billion 62 million 753 thousand 9.

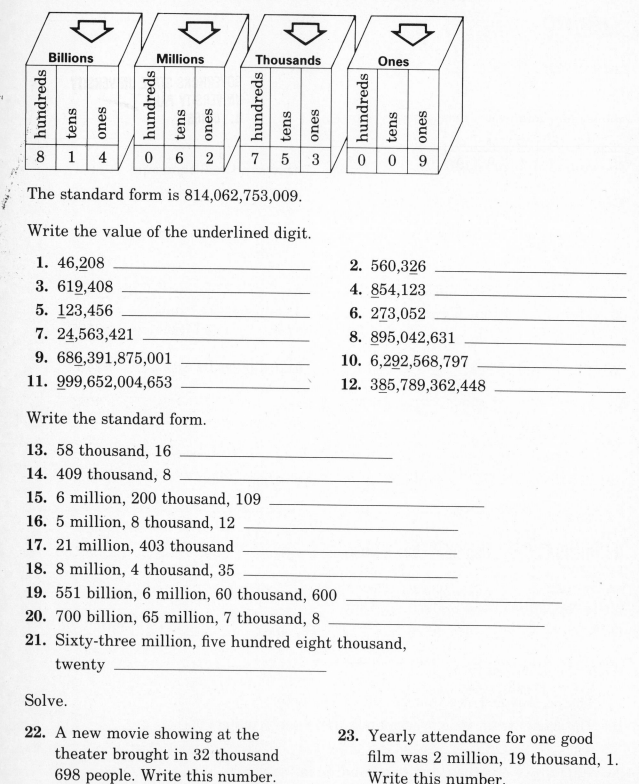

The standard form is 814,062,753,009.

Write the value of the underlined digit.

1. 46,2̲08 _____
2. 560,32̲6 _____
3. 619̲,408 _____
4. 8̲54,123 _____
5. 1̲23,456 _____
6. 27̲3,052 _____
7. 2̲4,563,421 _____
8. 895,04̲2,631 _____
9. 686̲,391,875,001 _____
10. 6,29̲2,568,797 _____
11. 9̲99,652,004,653 _____
12. 38̲5,789,362,448 _____

Write the standard form.

13. 58 thousand, 16 _____
14. 409 thousand, 8 _____
15. 6 million, 200 thousand, 109 _____
16. 5 million, 8 thousand, 12 _____
17. 21 million, 403 thousand _____
18. 8 million, 4 thousand, 35 _____
19. 551 billion, 6 million, 60 thousand, 600 _____
20. 700 billion, 65 million, 7 thousand, 8 _____
21. Sixty-three million, five hundred eight thousand, twenty _____

Solve.

22. A new movie showing at the theater brought in 32 thousand 698 people. Write this number.

_____

23. Yearly attendance for one good film was 2 million, 19 thousand, 1. Write this number.

_____

Practice

Compare 327,189 and 326,189.

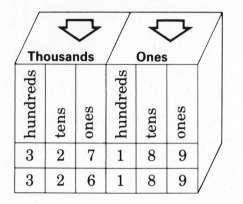

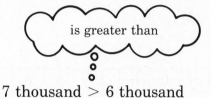

The hundred thousands are the same.
The ten thousands are the same.
The thousands are different.

is greater than

7 thousand > 6 thousand
so, 327,189 > 326,189

Write <, >, or = to compare the numbers.

1. 732 _____ 728   **2.** 809 _____ 813   **3.** 328 _____ 319

4. 607 _____ 670   **5.** 5124 _____ 4899   **6.** 8203 _____ 8197

7. 4518 _____ 4514   **8.** 5032 _____ 5120   **9.** 679 _____ 6243

10. 4013 _____ 4013   **11.** 4583 _____ 483   **12.** 3282 _____ 3282

13. 8109 _____ 8019   **14.** 4231 _____ 4132   **15.** 5816 _____ 518

16. 6124 _____ 5898   **17.** 8647 _____ 8900   **18.** 7216 _____ 896

19. 15,280 _____ 18,100 **20.** 29,053 _____ 92,053 **21.** 14,092 _____ 14,029

22. 62,325 _____ 62,325 **23.** 81,056 _____ 8156   **24.** 7918 _____ 69,180

25. 537,291 _____ 573,291 **26.** 728,015 _____ 728,014 **27.** 132,816 _____ 311,219

Order the numbers from least to greatest.

28. 24,860; 24,680; 24,068 _____

29. 465,000; 464,099; 464,999 _____

30. 327,846,393; 7,846,339; 7,846,933; 7,846,394

_____

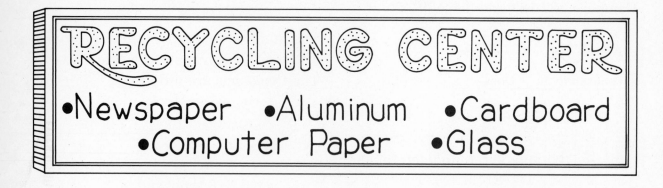

RECYCLING CENTER
•Newspaper •Aluminum •Cardboard
•Computer Paper •Glass

Solve.

1. The first customer of the morning brought in 7 bundles of newspaper. Last week the same customer brought in 6 bundles one day and 3 bundles the following day. How many bundles did this customer recycle? _____

2. A small company brought in some computer paper. The total weight was one thousand three hundred ninety-seven pounds. Write this number in standard form. _____

3. Last month Mike collected 236 lb of newspaper, Jennifer collected 326 lb and Carlos collected 362 lb. Who collected the most newspapers? _____

4. One day 2304 aluminum cans were brought in to the recycling center. Write this number in expanded form. _____

5. A pick-up truck delivered some glass bottles to the recycling center. It brought 347 green bottles, 256 clear bottles, 329 red bottles, and 401 blue bottles. Write the numbers in order from least to greatest. _____

6. Debbie collected 127 cardboard boxes and her friend Sue collected 145 cardboard boxes. Who collected more boxes? _____

7. On Friday there were 8 people working at the recycling center. On Saturday 9 people worked and on Sunday 6 people worked. How many people worked during the three days? _____

Name

Round 78 to the nearest ten. Since 78 is nearer 80 than 70, round 78 to 80.

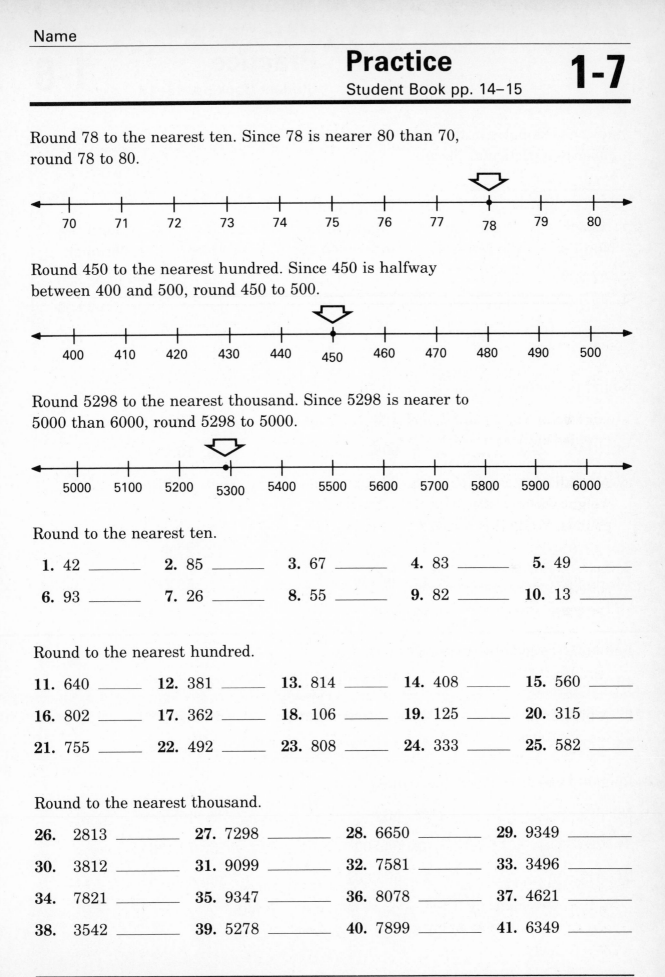

Round 450 to the nearest hundred. Since 450 is halfway between 400 and 500, round 450 to 500.

Round 5298 to the nearest thousand. Since 5298 is nearer to 5000 than 6000, round 5298 to 5000.

Round to the nearest ten.

1. 42 _____   2. 85 _____   3. 67 _____   4. 83 _____   5. 49 _____

6. 93 _____   7. 26 _____   8. 55 _____   9. 82 _____   10. 13 _____

Round to the nearest hundred.

11. 640 _____   12. 381 _____   13. 814 _____   14. 408 _____   15. 560 _____

16. 802 _____   17. 362 _____   18. 106 _____   19. 125 _____   20. 315 _____

21. 755 _____   22. 492 _____   23. 808 _____   24. 333 _____   25. 582 _____

Round to the nearest thousand.

26. 2813 _____   27. 7298 _____   28. 6650 _____   29. 9349 _____

30. 3812 _____   31. 9099 _____   32. 7581 _____   33. 3496 _____

34. 7821 _____   35. 9347 _____   36. 8078 _____   37. 4621 _____

38. 3542 _____   39. 5278 _____   40. 7899 _____   41. 6349 _____

Practice

Student Book pp. 16–17

1-8

Study the examples in the chart to learn how to round a
number to a particular place.

Exact Number	Round to the Nearest	Digit to the Right of the Underlined Digit	Is It 5 or More?	Round the Number
52,3<u>2</u>9	ten	9	yes	up to 52,330
62,<u>7</u>83	hundred	8	yes	up to 62,800
<u>1</u>221	thousand	2	no	down to 1000

Round to the nearest ten.

1. 827 _____

2. 193 _____

3. 5614 _____

4. 3148 _____

5. 6085 _____

6. 15,384 _____

7. 45,626 _____

8. 72,437 _____

9. 29,019 _____

Round to the nearest hundred.

10. 3270 _____

11. 5625 _____

12. 2739 _____

13. 15,689 _____

14. 29,732 _____

15. 58,119 _____

16. 856,372 _____

17. 419,319 _____

18. 567,831 _____

Round to the nearest thousand.

19. 35,900 _____

20. 63,187 _____

21. 12,934 _____

22. 86,042 _____

23. 325,168 _____

24. 157,929 _____

25. 706,758 _____

26. 841,056 _____

27. 463,542 _____

Round to the place of the underlined digit.

28. <u>3</u>92 _____

29. 56<u>3</u>8 _____

30. 49<u>8</u>5 _____

31. 2<u>6</u>,053 _____

32. 5<u>3</u>,900 _____

33. 72,<u>1</u>88 _____

34. 417,<u>0</u>39 _____

35. 598,<u>3</u>62 _____

36. 806,<u>7</u>38 _____

Name _____

Practice

Student Book pp. 18–19

1-9

Write the sum of 67 and 46.

Add the ones. Rename.

Rename 13 ones as 1 ten 3 ones.

Add the tens.

$$\begin{array}{r} 1 \\ 67 \\ +46 \\ \hline 3 \end{array}$$

$$\begin{array}{r} 1 \\ 67 \\ +46 \\ \hline 113 \end{array}$$

Add.

1. $\begin{array}{r} 38 \\ +56 \\ \hline \end{array}$
2. $\begin{array}{r} 49 \\ +72 \\ \hline \end{array}$
3. $\begin{array}{r} 48 \\ +\ 9 \\ \hline \end{array}$
4. $\begin{array}{r} 76 \\ +39 \\ \hline \end{array}$
5. $\begin{array}{r} 57 \\ +\ 8 \\ \hline \end{array}$

6. $\begin{array}{r} 782 \\ +384 \\ \hline \end{array}$
7. $\begin{array}{r} 842 \\ +967 \\ \hline \end{array}$
8. $\begin{array}{r} 921 \\ +184 \\ \hline \end{array}$
9. $\begin{array}{r} 794 \\ +162 \\ \hline \end{array}$
10. $\begin{array}{r} 445 \\ +815 \\ \hline \end{array}$

11. $\begin{array}{r} \$.45 \\ +\ .86 \\ \hline \end{array}$
12. $\begin{array}{r} \$.92 \\ +\ .09 \\ \hline \end{array}$
13. $\begin{array}{r} \$1.26 \\ +\ 2.17 \\ \hline \end{array}$
14. $\begin{array}{r} \$3.67 \\ +\ 6.86 \\ \hline \end{array}$
15. $\begin{array}{r} \$4.52 \\ +\ 2.99 \\ \hline \end{array}$

16. $\begin{array}{r} 73 \\ 56 \\ +92 \\ \hline \end{array}$
17. $\begin{array}{r} 41 \\ 36 \\ +27 \\ \hline \end{array}$
18. $\begin{array}{r} 92 \\ 48 \\ +25 \\ \hline \end{array}$
19. $\begin{array}{r} 763 \\ 52 \\ +365 \\ \hline \end{array}$
20. $\begin{array}{r} 399 \\ 162 \\ +283 \\ \hline \end{array}$

Solve.

21. During an inventory of art supplies at school, the teacher counted 26 jars of yellow paint, 15 jars of red paint, and 9 jars of blue paint.

    What is the total number of jars? _____

22. There are 156 packages of construction paper, 29 packages of tracing paper, and 9 packages of easel paper.

    How many packages of paper are there in all?

    _____

9 PA

Practice

1-10

Regional Speed Skating contests were held for a whole week in Northtown. This chart shows the attendance each day.

Monday	Tuesday	Wednesday	Thursday	Friday	Saturday	Sunday
68	85	98	132	248	378	347

Round each number to its greatest place value and then estimate the answer. Then find the exact answer.

1. How many people in all attended the races held on Monday and Friday?

Estimate: _____

Exact: _____

2. How many people in all attended the races held on Wednesday and Thursday?

Estimate: _____

Exact: _____

3. How many people in all attended the races held on Saturday and Sunday?

Estimate: _____

Exact: _____

4. How many people in all attended the races on Friday and Saturday?

Estimate: _____

Exact: _____

5. How many tickets were sold for Monday through Wednesday?

Estimate: _____

Exact: _____

6. How many people in all attended the races on Monday through Friday?

Estimate: _____

Exact: _____

7. How many people in all attended the races on Friday, Saturday, and Sunday?

Estimate: _____

Exact: _____

Name

Practice 1-11

Student Book pp. 22–23

Add 5374 and 3658.

Add the ones.	Add the tens.	Add the hundreds.	Add the thousands.
1	11	111	111
5374	5374	5374	5374
+3658	+3658	+3658	+3658
2	32	032	9032

Add.

1. 3846 + 5659

2. 7925 + 1286

3. 5361 + 854

4. 6727 + 518

5. 41,836 + 5,192

6. 65,283 + 4,798

7. 61,925 + 52,898

8. 53,936 + 38,887

9. 692,458 + 25,168

10. 491,682 + 337,895

11. 309,864 + 565,328

12. 9829, 1738 + 5625

Jetstar Motor Company Cars Produced–1986	
Large cars	2809
Mid-size cars	8315
Compact cars	6492

Draw a line to match each question to an exercise. Solve.

13. How many mid-size and compact cars were produced?

14. How many large cars and mid-size cars were produced?

15. How many large cars, mid-size cars and compact cars were produced in all?

A. 2809, 8315 + 6492

B. 8315 + 6492

C. 2809 + 8315

Practice
Student Book pp. 24–25

A charity organization held a rummage sale. Estimate these answers to the nearest dollar.

1. Several people contributed to the sale. Peggy brought items worth $164.39. Cleve brought things worth $189.80. About how much money was earned from their contributions? _____

2. Willard brought several things to be sold. He brought a saw that sold for $12.75, a level that sold for $6.50, and a work table that sold for $34.95. About how much was earned from these items? _____

3. Marge brought some items to be sold. She brought a sewing machine that sold for $66.95 and a picnic basket that sold for $19.25. About how much was earned from these items? _____

4. The first customer the second day bought a doll for $9.64 and a new coat for $14.39. About how much money did she spend? _____

5. The next customer bought a mirror for $12.38, a lamp for $21.92, and a set of dishes for $8.50. About how much did this customer spend? _____

6. Mrs. Hernandez bought a stroller for $16.60, a sweater for $8.30, and a bird cage for $13.85. About how much money did these items cost? _____

7. Mrs. Hernandez then decided to buy a box of records for $15.55. About how much did she spend all together? _____

Practice
Student Book pp. 34–35

Theona made 67 baskets during this season's games. Last season she made 39 baskets. How many more baskets did she make this season than last?

Rename 6 tens and 7 ones as 5 tens and 17 ones.

$$
\begin{array}{r}
\overset{5\ 17}{\cancel{6}\,\cancel{7}} \\
-\ 3\ 9 \\
\hline
\end{array}
$$

Subtract the ones.

$$
\begin{array}{r}
\overset{5\ 17}{\cancel{6}\,\cancel{7}} \\
-\ 3\ 9 \\
\hline
8
\end{array}
$$

Subtract the tens.

$$
\begin{array}{r}
\overset{5\ 17}{\cancel{6}\,\cancel{7}} \\
-\ 3\ 9 \\
\hline
2\ 8
\end{array}
$$

Theona made 28 more baskets this season.

Write the difference.

1. $\begin{array}{r}72\\-15\\\hline\end{array}$	**2.** $\begin{array}{r}56\\-\ 9\\\hline\end{array}$	**3.** $\begin{array}{r}81\\-23\\\hline\end{array}$	**4.** $\begin{array}{r}47\\-39\\\hline\end{array}$	**5.** $\begin{array}{r}72\\-56\\\hline\end{array}$
6. $\begin{array}{r}45\\-\ 7\\\hline\end{array}$	**7.** $\begin{array}{r}71\\-23\\\hline\end{array}$	**8.** $\begin{array}{r}53\\-14\\\hline\end{array}$	**9.** $\begin{array}{r}84\\-\ 5\\\hline\end{array}$	**10.** $\begin{array}{r}93\\-36\\\hline\end{array}$
11. $\begin{array}{r}638\\-453\\\hline\end{array}$	**12.** $\begin{array}{r}349\\-175\\\hline\end{array}$	**13.** $\begin{array}{r}664\\-138\\\hline\end{array}$	**14.** $\begin{array}{r}928\\-\ 79\\\hline\end{array}$	**15.** $\begin{array}{r}730\\-450\\\hline\end{array}$
16. $\begin{array}{r}\$.37\\-\ .18\\\hline\end{array}$	**17.** $\begin{array}{r}\$.98\\-\ .69\\\hline\end{array}$	**18.** $\begin{array}{r}\$.71\\-\ .34\\\hline\end{array}$	**19.** $\begin{array}{r}\$.86\\-\ .08\\\hline\end{array}$	**20.** $\begin{array}{r}\$.67\\-\ .38\\\hline\end{array}$

Solve.

21. Mr. Miller can type 76 words per minute. Ms. Brown can type 58 words per minute. How many more words per minute can Mr. Miller type than Ms. Brown? _____

Practice

Ring the hidden number.

1. Find the greatest 2-digit number that can be rounded to 40.

5421274318 46291282

2. Find the least 3-digit number that can be rounded to 100.

1639120521327 13142

3. Find the greatest number that can be rounded to 600.

736153823358959 1549

4. Find the greatest 4-digit number that can be rounded to 4000.

1734291124310 42331

5. Find the number that when rounded to the nearest hundred is 600.

67265018565 2968 66748

6. Find the least 3-digit number with all digits different and odd that can be rounded to 100.

237135715137 152134

7. Find the greatest 3-digit number with all digits different and even that can be rounded to 800.

85686368462 4816872

Practice

Subtract 3794 from 8362.

Rename the tens. Subtract the ones.	Rename the hundreds. Subtract the tens.	Rename the thousands. Subtract the hundreds.	Subtract the thousands.
$\begin{array}{r} \overset{5\ 12}{8\,3\,\cancel{6}\,\cancel{2}} \\ -3\,7\,9\,4 \\ \hline 8 \end{array}$	$\begin{array}{r} \overset{\ \ 15}{\underset{2\ \cancel{3}\ 12}{8\,\cancel{3}\,\cancel{6}\,\cancel{2}}} \\ -3\,7\,9\,4 \\ \hline 6\,8 \end{array}$	$\begin{array}{r} \overset{12\ 15}{7\,\cancel{3}\,\cancel{3}\,12} \\ \cancel{8}\,\cancel{3}\,\cancel{6}\,\cancel{2} \\ -3\,7\,9\,4 \\ \hline 5\,6\,8 \end{array}$	$\begin{array}{r} \overset{12\ 15}{7\,\cancel{3}\,\cancel{3}\,12} \\ \cancel{8}\,\cancel{3}\,\cancel{6}\,\cancel{2} \\ -3\,7\,9\,4 \\ \hline 4\,5\,6\,8 \end{array}$

Subtract.

1.	5274 − 886	**2.**	6437 − 798	**3.**	8248 −3865	**4.**	7659 −3673
5.	8246 −3452	**6.**	65,891 −29,937	**7.**	54,132 − 2,861	**8.**	75,386 − 2,589
9.	286,354 − 95,286	**10.**	639,877 −278,995	**11.**	72,506 − 3,705	**12.**	863,747 −169,591
13.	$ 5.64 − 2.85	**14.**	$8.28 − 5.39	**15.**	$427.35 − 15.96	**16.**	$687.28 − 325.99

17. 2563 − 178 = _____

18. 5427 − 889 = _____

19. 7454 − 3589 = _____

20. 71,464 − 6752 = _____

Solve.

21. There are 4532 apartments in the new Center City Apartment Complex. There are 463 apartments that have not yet been rented. How many apartments have been rented? _____

Name

Practice 2-4

Student Book pp. 40–41

Subtract 1535 from 6000.
There are no tens. There are no hundreds. So, we need to rename a thousand.

	Rename 600 tens as 599 tens and 10 ones.	Subtract.
6000 − 1535	599 10 ~~6000~~ − 1535	599 10 ~~6000~~ − 1535 4465

Write the difference.

1. 60 − 21	**2.** 80 − 39	**3.** 500 − 156	**4.** 700 − 519
5. 5006 − 3247	**6.** 4008 − 2119	**7.** 5060 − 3295	**8.** 7020 − 4562
9. 30,200 − 19,764	**10.** 50,040 − 12,352	**11.** 408,000 − 218,673	**12.** 700,300 − 243,561
13. $50.00 − 13.87	**14.** $72.00 − 26.35	**15.** $40.00 − 32.56	**16.** $80.20 − 15.65

17. 5000 − 652 = ________ **18.** 7600 − 823 = ________

19. 5003 − 1245 = ________ **20.** 8050 − 596 = ________

Solve.

21. There are 4030 students enrolled at the high school and 763 students enrolled at the elementary school. How many more students are enrolled at the high school than at the elementary school? ________

Practice

Student Book pp. 42–43

Write in order each coin that you would give in change.
Use the fewest coins possible. Write *p* for penny, *n* for nickel,
d for dime, *q* for quarter, and *hd* for half-dollar.

	Amount Spent	Amount to Cashier	Change Received
1.	17¢	25¢	_____
2.	23¢	30¢	_____
3.	27¢	50¢	_____
4.	41¢	$1	_____
5.	54¢	$1	_____
6.	61¢	75¢	_____
7.	18¢	50¢	_____
8.	21¢	$1	_____

Is the change correct? If not, write a correct amount of change.

	Amount Spent	Amount to Cashier	Change Received	
9.	13¢	25¢	2p, 1n, 1d	_____
10.	11¢	30¢	4p, 1n, 1d	_____
11.	37¢	$1	3p, 1n, 1hd	_____
12.	56¢	$1	1p, 4d	_____
13.	67¢	$1	3p, 1n, 1q	_____
14.	19¢	$1	1p, 8d	_____

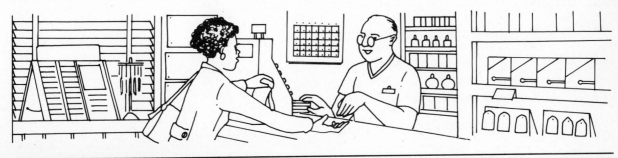

Name _____

Arrowhead	78,034
Empire	32,759
Las Vegas	16,110
Pontiac	80,399
Rose Bowl	106,721
Schaefer	61,279
Soldier Field	55,701

The table shows the seating capacity of 7 stadiums.

What is the seating capacity, rounded to the nearest thousand?

1. Schaefer _____   **2.** Pontiac _____   **3.** Rose Bowl _____

What is the seating capacity, rounded to the nearest ten thousand?

4. Arrowhead _____   **5.** Empire _____   **6.** Soldier Field _____

What is the combined seating capacity?

7. Arrowhead and Las Vegas _____

8. Empire and Rose Bowl _____

9. Soldier Field and Rose Bowl _____

What is the difference in seating capacity?

10. between Arrowhead and Schaefer _____

11. between Rose Bowl and Las Vegas _____

12. between Pontiac and Soldier Field _____

How many empty seats are there?

13. 55,286 people in Soldier Field _____

14. 101,294 people in the Rose Bowl _____

15. 49,581 people in Schaefer Stadium _____

16. 29,830 people in Empire Stadium _____

17. 73,462 people in Pontiac Stadium _____

18. 75,938 people in Arrowhead Stadium _____

Name _____

Measure to the nearest centimeter and millimeter.

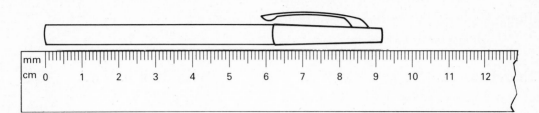

To the nearest centimeter, the pen is 9 cm long. To the nearest millimeter, the pen is 92 mm long.

Use a centimeter ruler. Measure to the nearest centimeter.

1. _____   _____   2. _____   _____

3. _____   _____   4. _____   _____

5. _____   _____

6. _____   _____

7. _____   _____

8. _____   _____

9. _____   _____

10. _____   _____

Measure to the nearest millimeter.

11. _____   _____   12. _____   _____

13. ___   _____   14. _____   _____

15. _____   _____

16. _____   _____

17. _____   _____

18. _____   _____

19. _____   _____

20. _____   _____

Which is longer?

21. A pencil that is 15 cm long or a pen that is 155 mm long.   _____

22. A stick that is 50 cm long or a board that is 7 dm long.   _____

Practice

The meter (m) is a standard unit for measuring length.

$$1 \text{ m} = 100 \text{ cm}$$

The kilometer (km) is used to measure long distances.

$$1 \text{ km} = 1000 \text{ m}$$

Your thumbnail is about 1 cm wide.

Your desk is about 1 m high.

You will run 1 km if you run from goal post to goal post ten times on a soccer field.

Complete. Write cm, m, or km.

1. A car is about 4 _____ long.

2. A stapler is about 20 _____ long.

3. A calculator is about 15 _____ long.

4. A mountain is about 4 _____ high.

5. A swimming pool is about 2 _____ deep.

6. A car drove about 80 _____ per hour.

7. A ceiling is about 3 _____ high.

8. Your finger is about 6 _____ long.

Circle the most likely measurement.

9.	the length of a table	2 cm	2 m	2 km
10.	the distance you can broad jump	1 cm	1 m	1 km
11.	the length of your hand	12 cm	12 m	12 km
12.	the height of a ladder	2 cm	2 m	2 km
13.	the width of a math book	18 cm	18 m	18 km
14.	the distance from home to school	3 cm	3 m	3 km
15.	the height of a volleyball net	2 cm	2 m	2 km
16.	the length of a baseball bat	1 cm	1 m	1 km
17.	the length of a swimming pool	20 cm	20 m	20 km
18.	the length of a room	5 cm	5 m	5 km

Name _____

Circle the better estimate.

1.  Joe needs about
1 mL   1L
of glue.

2.  The pitcher holds
1 mL   1L
of milk.

3.  The feather
has a mass of
about
1 g   1 kg

4.  The kitten
has a mass of
about
1 g   1 kg

Estimate the measurement. Write mL, L, kg, or g to complete.

5. A glass holds about 250 _____.

6. A bathtub holds about 150 _____.

7. A spoon holds about 2 _____.

8. A carton of juice holds about 1 _____.

9. A potato has a mass of about
200 _____.

10. A baby has a mass of about
3 _____.

Circle the best estimate.

11. the gas tank of a car	60 mL	60 L	600 L
12. a drop of medicine	1 mL	1 L	10 L
13. a can of paint	4 mL	4 L	400L
14. the mass of a quarter	5 g	5 kg	50 kg
15. the mass of a student	38 g	38 kg	380 kg
16. the mass of a basketball	5 g	560 g	560 kg
17. the mass of a loaf of bread	454 g	4 kg	40 kg
18. the mass of a chicken	3 g	3 kg	30 kg
19. the mass of a hair clip	2 g	200 g	2 kg
20. the mass of a pear	2 g	200 g	2 kg
21. the mass of a peanut	2 g	200 g	2 kg

Practice

2-10

$$\xleftarrow{\hspace{1cm}} \overset{|}{-20} \quad \overset{|}{-15} \quad \overset{|}{-10} \quad \overset{|}{-5} \quad \overset{|}{0} \quad \overset{|}{5} \quad \overset{|}{10} \quad \overset{|}{15} \quad \overset{|}{20} \quad \overset{|}{25} \quad \overset{|}{30} \quad \overset{|}{35} \quad \overset{|}{40} \xrightarrow{\hspace{1cm}}$$

The number line shows temperatures on the Celsius Scale. Temperatures to the left of 0 are below zero. ⁻10° is read "10 degrees below zero."

What is the increase in temperature?

1. from 4° to 12° _____

2. from 8° to 28° _____

3. from 0° to 17° _____

4. from ⁻4° to 12° _____

5. from ⁻2° to 4° _____

6. from ⁻14 to ⁻5° _____

What is the drop in temperature?

7. from 36° to 15° _____

8. from 48° to 29° _____

9. from 17° to ⁻3° _____

10. from 53° to ⁻47° _____

11. from ⁻6° to ⁻15° _____

12. from ⁻23° to ⁻48° _____

What is the temperature after the change?

13. an increase of 6° from 4° _____

14. an increase of 7° from 0° _____

15. an increase of 8° from ⁻4° _____

16. an increase of 12° from ⁻14° _____

17. a drop of 22° from 29° _____

18. a drop of 20° from 14° _____

19. a drop of 6° from 0° _____

20. a drop of 3° from ⁻7° _____

What was the original temperature?

21. It is now 14° after a drop of 26°. _____

22. It is now ⁻2° after a drop of 18°. _____

23. It is now 7° after an increase of 13°. _____

24. It is now ⁻4° after an increase of 11°. _____

25. It is now 8° after an increase of 25°. _____

Practice

Student Book pp. 54–55

Circle the best estimate.

1.  The length of a
paper clip

1 in.   1 ft   1 yd

2.  The height of a
wastebasket

1 in.   1 ft   1 yd

3.  The height of
a table

1 in.   1 ft   1 yd

4. 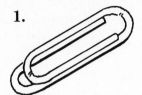 The height of a
mountain

1 ft   1 yd   1 mi

Estimate. Write in., ft, yd, or mi.

5. A key is about 2 _____ long.

6. The thickness of a math book is about 1 _____ .

7. A river is about 3 _____ long.

8. A swimming pool is about 8 _____ deep.

9. A stove is about 1 _____ high.

Circle the best estimate.

10. the height of a basketball hoop   9 in.   9 ft   9 yd

11. the amount of fabric needed to   3 in.   3 yd   3 mi
make a dress

12. the length of a pencil   7 in.   7 ft   7 yd

13. the length of a street   3 ft   3 yd   3 mi

14. the length of a hand   6 in.   6 ft   6 yd

Add or subtract.

15.   8 ft 3 in.   **16.**   2 ft 8 in.   **17.**   5 yd 1 ft   **18.**   9 yd 1 ft
        + 9 ft 2 in.   + 6 ft 3 in.   + 3 yd 1 ft   + 3 yd 1 ft

19.   7 yd 2 ft   **20.**   4 mi 516 ft   **21.**   8 ft 11 in.   **22.**   14 yd 2 ft
        − 4 yd 1 ft   − 3 mi 248 ft   − 6 ft 3 in.   − 6 yd 1 ft

Practice
Student Book pp. 56–57

2-12

Circle the best estimate.

1.

The pebbles weigh about

2 oz   2 lb   2 t

2.

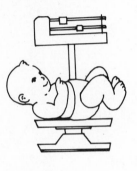

The newborn baby weighs about

6 oz   6 lb   6 t

3.

The truck weighs about

9 oz   9 lb   9 t

Circle the best estimate.

4. a glass of milk holds about	1 c	1 pt	1 qt
5. the gas tank of a car holds about	15 c	15 pt	15 gal
6. a can of paint holds about	1 gal	10 gal	100 gal
7. a small can of peas holds about	1 c	1 qt	1 gal
8. a container of juice holds about	1 qt	10 qt	100 qt
9. a loaf of bread weighs about	16 oz	16 lb	16 t
10. five students weigh about	35 oz	35 lb	350 lb
11. a car weighs about	300 lb	3000 lb	3000 t
12. an orange weighs about	4 oz	4 lb	4 t
13. a hippo weighs about	1 oz	1 lb	1 t

Solve.

14. A certain recipe calls for 7 oz of butter. The baker has 15 oz of butter. How much butter will be left over? _____

15. Which is greater, 4 lb or 65 oz? _____

Practice

Student Book pp. 66–67

3-1

There are 9 players on a baseball team. Each league has 5 teams. To find the total number of players, add or multiply.

$$9 + 9 + 9 + 9 + 9 = 45$$

$$
\begin{array}{rl}
 & \text{factor} \longrightarrow 9 \\
5 \times 9 = 45 & \text{factor} \longrightarrow \times 5 \\
 & \text{product} \longrightarrow 45
\end{array}
$$

There are 45 players in each league.

These rules will help you memorize the multiplication facts.

The Commutative Property	
Changing the order of the factors does not change the product.	$8 \times 2 = 16$ $2 \times 8 = 16$ so $8 \times 2 = 2 \times 8$
The Property of One	
The product of one and any number is that number.	$2 \times 1 = 2$ $9 \times 1 = 9$
The Zero Property	
The product of zero and any number is zero.	$8 \times 0 = 0$ $0 \times 4 = 0$

Multiply.

1. $\begin{array}{r} 8 \\ \times 2 \\ \hline \end{array}$
2. $\begin{array}{r} 5 \\ \times 5 \\ \hline \end{array}$
3. $\begin{array}{r} 9 \\ \times 2 \\ \hline \end{array}$
4. $\begin{array}{r} 9 \\ \times 3 \\ \hline \end{array}$
5. $\begin{array}{r} 4 \\ \times 8 \\ \hline \end{array}$
6. $\begin{array}{r} 9 \\ \times 8 \\ \hline \end{array}$

7. $\begin{array}{r} 6 \\ \times 7 \\ \hline \end{array}$
8. $\begin{array}{r} 8 \\ \times 5 \\ \hline \end{array}$
9. $\begin{array}{r} 4 \\ \times 9 \\ \hline \end{array}$
10. $\begin{array}{r} 0 \\ \times 6 \\ \hline \end{array}$
11. $\begin{array}{r} 7 \\ \times 8 \\ \hline \end{array}$
12. $\begin{array}{r} 4 \\ \times 6 \\ \hline \end{array}$

13. $\begin{array}{r} 7 \\ \times 7 \\ \hline \end{array}$
14. $\begin{array}{r} 8 \\ \times 8 \\ \hline \end{array}$
15. $\begin{array}{r} 2 \\ \times 4 \\ \hline \end{array}$
16. $\begin{array}{r} 3 \\ \times 7 \\ \hline \end{array}$
17. $\begin{array}{r} 6 \\ \times 8 \\ \hline \end{array}$
18. $\begin{array}{r} 7 \\ \times 9 \\ \hline \end{array}$

19. $\begin{array}{r} 0 \\ \times 5 \\ \hline \end{array}$
20. $\begin{array}{r} 6 \\ \times 6 \\ \hline \end{array}$
21. $\begin{array}{r} 4 \\ \times 1 \\ \hline \end{array}$
22. $\begin{array}{r} 9 \\ \times 3 \\ \hline \end{array}$
23. $\begin{array}{r} 4 \\ \times 4 \\ \hline \end{array}$
24. $\begin{array}{r} 5 \\ \times 7 \\ \hline \end{array}$

Practice

Student Book pp. 68–69

3-2

Associative Property

Changing the grouping of the factors does not change the product.

$(2 \times 2) \times 3 = 12$ $2 \times (2 \times 3) = 12$

so $(2 \times 2) \times 3 = 2 \times (2 \times 3)$

Use number patterns when multiplying 3 or more numbers.

$6 \times (5 \times 2) = 6 \times 10 = 60$

Multiply.

1. $3 \times 5 \times 2 =$ _____
2. $5 \times 4 \times 3 =$ _____
3. $6 \times 1 \times 4 =$ _____

4. $2 \times 3 \times 2 =$ _____
5. $9 \times 5 \times 2 =$ _____
6. $5 \times 2 \times 2 =$ _____

7. $5 \times 2 \times 5 =$ _____
8. $3 \times 2 \times 5 =$ _____
9. $6 \times 5 \times 2 =$ _____

10. $7 \times 2 \times 2 =$ _____
11. $8 \times 0 \times 9 =$ _____
12. $3 \times 2 \times 9 =$ _____

13. $6 \times 2 \times 10 =$ _____
14. $3 \times 2 \times 6 =$ _____
15. $5 \times 2 \times 3 =$ _____

16. $7 \times 10 \times 4 =$ _____
17. $2 \times 5 \times 2 =$ _____
18. $7 \times 9 \times 0 =$ _____

19. $10 \times 5 \times 4 =$ _____
20. $8 \times 10 \times 2 =$ _____
21. $4 \times 0 \times 9 =$ _____

22. $6 \times 2 \times 5 =$ _____
23. $3 \times 3 \times 5 =$ _____
24. $4 \times 2 \times 9 =$ _____

Solve.

25. Jill bought 2 bunches of bananas at the supermarket. Each bunch had 5 bananas. She cut each banana into 3 pieces. How many pieces did she have in all?

_____

26. Matt bought 2 packages of tomatoes. Each package had 4 tomatoes. He cut each tomato into 6 slices. How many tomato slices did Matt have altogether?

_____

Name _____

Practice
Student Book pp. 70–71

3-3

Here is an example of the **Distributive Property**.

$4 \times (2 + 1) = 12$ $\qquad\qquad\qquad$ $(4 \times 2) + (4 \times 1) = 12$

so $4 \times (2 + 1) = (4 \times 2) + (4 \times 1)$

Use the Distributive Property to multiply 52 by 4.	You can also multiply this way.	
Rewrite one factor. $4 \times (50 + 2)$ Multiply. $(4 \times 50) + (4 \times 2)$ Add. $200 + 8 = 208$	Multiply 2 ones by 4. $\begin{array}{r} 52 \\ \times 4 \\ \hline 8 \end{array}$	Multiply 5 tens by 4. $\begin{array}{r} 52 \\ \times 4 \\ \hline 208 \end{array}$

When you multiply 28×4, you need to rename.

Multiply 8 ones by 4.
Rename 32 ones as 3 tens 2 ones.

$$\begin{array}{r} {\scriptstyle 3} \\ 28 \\ \times 4 \\ \hline 2 \end{array}$$

Multiply 2 tens by 4.
Then add the 3 tens.

$$\begin{array}{r} {\scriptstyle 3} \\ 28 \\ \times 4 \\ \hline 112 \end{array}$$

Multiply.

1. $\begin{array}{r} 37 \\ \times 4 \\ \hline \end{array}$
2. $\begin{array}{r} 49 \\ \times 6 \\ \hline \end{array}$
3. $\begin{array}{r} 56 \\ \times 4 \\ \hline \end{array}$
4. $\begin{array}{r} 56 \\ \times 2 \\ \hline \end{array}$
5. $\begin{array}{r} 48 \\ \times 7 \\ \hline \end{array}$
6. $\begin{array}{r} 70 \\ \times 5 \\ \hline \end{array}$

7. $\begin{array}{r} 93 \\ \times 7 \\ \hline \end{array}$
8. $\begin{array}{r} 45 \\ \times 8 \\ \hline \end{array}$
9. $\begin{array}{r} 62 \\ \times 9 \\ \hline \end{array}$
10. $\begin{array}{r} 74 \\ \times 7 \\ \hline \end{array}$
11. $\begin{array}{r} 89 \\ \times 5 \\ \hline \end{array}$
12. $\begin{array}{r} 31 \\ \times 6 \\ \hline \end{array}$

13. $\begin{array}{r} 35 \\ \times 4 \\ \hline \end{array}$
14. $\begin{array}{r} 79 \\ \times 6 \\ \hline \end{array}$
15. $\begin{array}{r} 84 \\ \times 7 \\ \hline \end{array}$
16. $\begin{array}{r} 96 \\ \times 5 \\ \hline \end{array}$
17. $\begin{array}{r} 39 \\ \times 4 \\ \hline \end{array}$
18. $\begin{array}{r} 82 \\ \times 7 \\ \hline \end{array}$

19. $3 \times 41 = $ _____

20. $6 \times 48 = $ _____

21. $3 \times 88 = $ _____

22. $2 \times 37 = $ _____

23. $8 \times 70 = $ _____

24. $5 \times 75 = $ _____

25. $4 \times 96 = $ _____

26. $4 \times 52 = $ _____

27. $9 \times 56 = $ _____

Practice

Student Book pp. 72–73

3-4

There are 5 ski lifts at High Mountain Ski Bowl. Each lift can carry 342 people in one hour. How many skiers can all 5 lifts carry in one hour?

Multiply 342 by 5.

Multiply 2 ones by 5. $5 \times 2 = 10$ Write the 0. Remember the 1 ten.	Multiply 4 tens by 5 and add the 1 ten. $5 \times 4 = 20$ $20 + 1 = 21$ Write the 1. Remember the 2 hundreds.	Multiply 3 hundreds by 5 and add the 2 hundreds.
342 ×5 ―― 0	342 ×5 ―― 10	342 ×5 ―― 1710

In one hour, 1710 skiers can ride up the mountain.

Multiply.

1. 394 ×4	**2.** 428 ×6	**3.** 574 ×7	**4.** 839 ×5	**5.** 848 ×3
6. 3908 ×5	**7.** 6145 ×6	**8.** 7914 ×8	**9.** 3293 ×7	**10.** 9142 ×9
11. 7125 ×4	**12.** 3987 ×8	**13.** 2963 ×5	**14.** 5416 ×7	**15.** 3908 ×9

16. $4 \times 796 =$ _____ **17.** $3 \times 708 =$ _____ **18.** $9 \times 543 =$ _____

19. $8 \times 1938 =$ _____ **20.** $6 \times 2470 =$ _____ **21.** $5 \times 2471 =$ _____

Solve.

22. The school store sold binders for $2 each. On Tuesday, 190 students bought binders. How much money did the school store collect? _____

Practice

Student Book pp. 74–75

During a snowstorm, the speed limit on the turnpike was lowered to 40 mi/h. Ann drove at the speed limit for 2 h. How many miles did she travel?

Multiply 40 by 2, to find the answer.

$$\begin{array}{r} 40 \\ \times\,2 \\ \hline 80 \end{array}$$ Ann traveled 80 mi.

This chart shows how many miles Ann can travel in 1, 2, 3, and 4 hours.

number of hours	1	2	3	4
miles traveled	40	80	120	160

Complete the chart.

1. There are 12 in. in a foot.

number of feet	2	4	6	8
number of inches				

2. Ann works 6 h per day.

number of days	3	6	9	12
number of hours				

3. There are 3 ft in a yard.

number of yards	10	20	30	40
number of feet				

Solve.

4. Carlos spends 4 h every day mowing lawns. How many hours does he spend mowing lawns each week? _____

5. The cafeteria serves about 230 lunches each school day. About how many lunches are served each week? _____

Practice
Student Book pp. 76–77

3-6

This chart shows the number of cars on one road on an average day.

Time (AM)	Number of cars	Time (PM)	Number of cars
5:00-6:00	480	3:00-4:00	398
6:00-7:00	570	4:00-5:00	586
7:00-8:00	610	5:00-6:00	714
8:00-9:00	506	6:00-7:00	607
9:00-10:00	394	7:00-8:00	423

1. At what time of day is traffic the lightest? _____

2. At what time of day is traffic the heaviest? _____

3. During what 2 h period is traffic the heaviest? _____

4. How many cars travel this highway between 3:00 PM and 8:00 PM? _____

5. How many cars travel the highway between 6:00-7:00 AM Monday through Friday? _____

6. How many cars travel the highway between 5:00-6:00 PM Monday through Friday? _____

7. How many cars travel the highway between 6:00-9:00 AM Monday through Friday? _____

8. How many cars travel the highway between 5:00-10:00 AM Monday through Friday? _____

9. How many cars travel the highway between 3:00-8:00 PM Monday through Friday? _____

10. How many cars travel the highway both AM and PM Monday through Friday? _____

Practice

Student Book pp. 78–79

3-7

Study these problems and find a pattern.

$$\begin{array}{ccc} 24 & 24 & 24 \\ \times 3 & \times 30 & \times 300 \\ \hline 72 & 720 & 7200 \end{array}$$

Hint: Look at the number of zeros in the factors. Then look at the number of zeros in the product.

When multiplying with multiples of 100, you can use a short cut.

$$\begin{array}{c} 64 \\ \times 5 \\ \hline 320 \end{array}$$

$$\begin{array}{c} 640 \\ \times 500 \\ \hline 320,000 \end{array}$$

Count the number of zeros in the factors. Add that many zeros to the end of the product.

Multiply.

1. $\begin{array}{r} 38 \\ \times 40 \\ \hline \end{array}$	**2.** $\begin{array}{r} 438 \\ \times 800 \\ \hline \end{array}$	**3.** $\begin{array}{r} 26 \\ \times 30 \\ \hline \end{array}$	**4.** $\begin{array}{r} 78 \\ \times 50 \\ \hline \end{array}$	**5.** $\begin{array}{r} 34 \\ \times 600 \\ \hline \end{array}$
6. $\begin{array}{r} 168 \\ \times 20 \\ \hline \end{array}$	**7.** $\begin{array}{r} 39 \\ \times 300 \\ \hline \end{array}$	**8.** $\begin{array}{r} 84 \\ \times 40 \\ \hline \end{array}$	**9.** $\begin{array}{r} 325 \\ \times 500 \\ \hline \end{array}$	**10.** $\begin{array}{r} 566 \\ \times 40 \\ \hline \end{array}$
11. $\begin{array}{r} 42 \\ \times 300 \\ \hline \end{array}$	**12.** $\begin{array}{r} 293 \\ \times 400 \\ \hline \end{array}$	**13.** $\begin{array}{r} 538 \\ \times 70 \\ \hline \end{array}$	**14.** $\begin{array}{r} 336 \\ \times 50 \\ \hline \end{array}$	**15.** $\begin{array}{r} 35 \\ \times 30 \\ \hline \end{array}$

16. $20 \times 26 =$ _____ **17.** $50 \times 49 =$ _____ **18.** $60 \times 524 =$ _____

19. $\begin{array}{r} 4000 \\ \times 200 \\ \hline \end{array}$	**20.** $\begin{array}{r} 6000 \\ \times 300 \\ \hline \end{array}$	**21.** $\begin{array}{r} 8000 \\ \times 200 \\ \hline \end{array}$	**22.** $\begin{array}{r} 3600 \\ \times 500 \\ \hline \end{array}$	**23.** $\begin{array}{r} 5400 \\ \times 2000 \\ \hline \end{array}$
24. $\begin{array}{r} 4700 \\ \times 400 \\ \hline \end{array}$	**25.** $\begin{array}{r} 3200 \\ \times 800 \\ \hline \end{array}$	**26.** $\begin{array}{r} 8800 \\ \times 6000 \\ \hline \end{array}$	**27.** $\begin{array}{r} 32,400 \\ \times 5,000 \\ \hline \end{array}$	**28.** $\begin{array}{r} 59,800 \\ \times 400 \\ \hline \end{array}$

Solve.

29. There are 500 sheets of typing paper in a box. A secretary ordered 25 boxes of paper. How many sheets of paper did he order? _____

Name _____

Estimate 24 × 13.

You can estimate by rounding each factor to its greatest place value.

$$\begin{array}{r} 24 \longrightarrow 20 \\ \times 13 \longrightarrow \times 10 \\ \hline 200 \end{array}$$

You can estimate by rounding one factor up and one factor down.

$$\begin{array}{r} 24 \longrightarrow 30 \\ \times 13 \longrightarrow \times 10 \\ \hline 300 \end{array}$$

The second estimate is closer to the exact product.

Round each factor with more than one digit to its greatest place value. Then estimate the product.

1. 56 × 3	**2.** 84 × 9	**3.** 359 × 15	**4.** 465 × 88
5. 392 × 73	**6.** 830 × 6	**7.** 483 × 3	**8.** 888 × 22

Round one factor up and one factor down. Estimate the product.

9. 72 × 16	**10.** 94 × 18	**11.** 38 × 12	**12.** 86 × 43
13. 475 × 14	**14.** 782 × 14	**15.** 391 × 42	**16.** 706 × 55
17. 255 × 21	**18.** 398 × 412	**19.** 604 × 96	**20.** 781 × 22

Solve.

21. Greta bought 24 dresses for her shop. Each dress cost $19.95. Estimate how much she spent altogether. _____

22. Greta bought 36 sweaters at $8.90 each. Estimate how much the sweaters cost. _____

Name _____

Multiply.

1. 76 ×35	**2.** 48 ×34	**3.** 19 ×52	**4.** 89 ×61	**5.** 72 ×29
6. 41 ×47	**7.** 23 ×48	**8.** 59 ×16	**9.** 61 ×79	**10.** 82 ×83
11. 59 ×11	**12.** 92 ×85	**13.** 63 ×42	**14.** 85 ×37	**15.** 76 ×46
16. 77 ×88	**17.** 61 ×79	**18.** 82 ×19	**19.** 25 ×35	**20.** 36 ×44

Solve.

21. There were 73 children who participated in the school walkathon. If each child walked 12 mi, how many miles did they walk in all? _____

22. There were 24 children that made posters for the walkathon. If each child made 13 posters, how many posters did they make in all?

    _____

23. The walkathon ended at the school stadium. There are 65 rows of seats in the stadium. Each row has 85 seats. How many seats are there in all? _____

Practice
Student Book pp. 84–85

3-10

One Sunday, the Boston Tribune had 236 pages. Carlos delivered the paper to 63 homes. What was the total number of pages he carried?

Multiply 236 × 3.	Multiply 236 × 60.	Add the products.
236 ×63 708	236 ×63 708 14160	236 ×63 708 14 160 14,868

Carlos carried 14,868 pages.

Multiply.

1. 649 ×27	2. 307 ×65	3. 453 ×48	4. 987 ×72	5. 325 ×55

6. 756 ×43	7. 985 ×78	8. 612 ×36	9. 419 ×25	10. 720 ×49

11. 6591 ×27	12. 3104 ×65	13. 9858 ×32	14. 7911 ×47	15. 6015 ×48

16. 89 × 234 = _____   **17.** 61 × 2593 = _____   **18.** 46 × 835 = _____

Solve.

19. There are 38 trucks delivering cartons to stores. Each truck delivers 209 cartons. How many cartons are delivered in all?

_____

Name

Multiply 683 by 491.

Multiply 683 by 1.	Multiply 683 by 90.	Multiply 683 by 400.	Add the products.
683 ×491 —— 683	683 ×491 —— 683 61470	683 ×491 —— 683 61470 273200	683 ×491 —— 683 61 470 273 200 ———— 335,353

Remember:

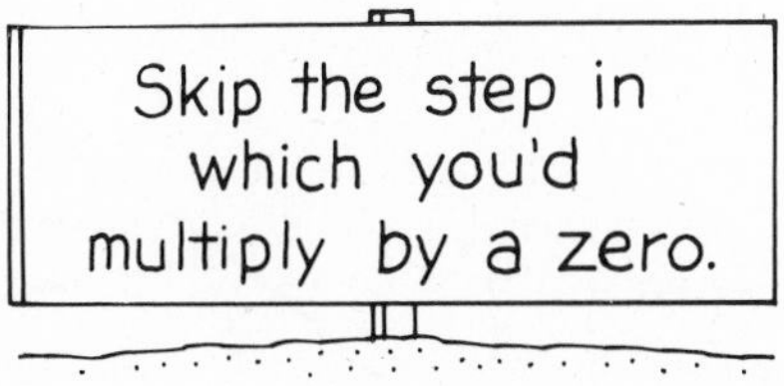

Skip the step in which you'd multiply by a zero.

$$\begin{array}{r} 381 \\ \times 480 \\ \hline 30\ 480 \\ 152\ 400 \\ \hline 182,880 \end{array}$$ o o o Skip this step.

Multiply.

1. 794
×635

2. 826
×543

3. 638
×208

4. 935
×786

5. 239
×459

6. 809
×321

7. 659
×188

8. 729
×604

9. 982
×936

10. 128
×845

11. 698
×564

12. 312
×705

13. 398
×128

14. 491
×835

15. 574
×834

16. 594 × 696 = _____

17. 381 × 294 = _____

18. 518 × 961 = _____

19. 428 × 367 = _____

Practice

Student Book pp. 88–89

3-12

Complete the tree diagram to solve. Then multiply to check.

1. You can have a cheese or a ham sandwich on white, wheat, or rye bread. How many different kinds of sandwiches can you have?

   cheese

   ham

   _____

2. To get to school, you can either walk or ride your bike. You can travel along Avenues A, B, C, or D. How many different ways can you get to school?

   walk

   ride your bike

   _____

3. After school, you can read, do homework, or work at the computer from 4 to 5. You can then watch TV, write letters, or talk on the phone from 5 to 6. How many different ways can you spend the time from 4 to 6? _____

Use the tree diagram to solve.

4. How many different choices of dinners do you have if you want fish? _____

5. How many different choices of dinners do you have if you want a salad? _____

6. If you want either peas or carrots, how many choices do you have?

   _____

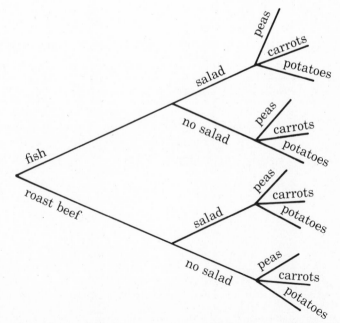

Name

How much would 8 carnations cost?
To find out, multiply $.98 by 8.

$$\begin{array}{r} \$\ .98 \\ \times 8 \\ \hline \$7.84 \end{array}$$

Eight carnations would cost $7.84.

Multiply.

1. $\begin{array}{r} \$\ .38 \\ \times 4 \\ \hline \end{array}$	2. $\begin{array}{r} \$\ .58 \\ \times 8 \\ \hline \end{array}$	3. $\begin{array}{r} \$\ .76 \\ \times 5 \\ \hline \end{array}$	4. $\begin{array}{r} \$\ .93 \\ \times 9 \\ \hline \end{array}$	5. $\begin{array}{r} \$\ .39 \\ \times 7 \\ \hline \end{array}$
6. $\begin{array}{r} \$1.35 \\ \times 2 \\ \hline \end{array}$	7. $\begin{array}{r} \$2.16 \\ \times 8 \\ \hline \end{array}$	8. $\begin{array}{r} \$1.98 \\ \times 4 \\ \hline \end{array}$	9. $\begin{array}{r} \$6.76 \\ \times 5 \\ \hline \end{array}$	10. $\begin{array}{r} \$9.18 \\ \times 3 \\ \hline \end{array}$
11. $\begin{array}{r} \$2.15 \\ \times 48 \\ \hline \end{array}$	12. $\begin{array}{r} \$7.32 \\ \times 56 \\ \hline \end{array}$	13. $\begin{array}{r} \$9.05 \\ \times 32 \\ \hline \end{array}$	14. $\begin{array}{r} \$\ .69 \\ \times 84 \\ \hline \end{array}$	15. $\begin{array}{r} \$\ .79 \\ \times 39 \\ \hline \end{array}$
16. $\begin{array}{r} \$7.95 \\ \times 841 \\ \hline \end{array}$	17. $\begin{array}{r} \$9.25 \\ \times 537 \\ \hline \end{array}$	18. $\begin{array}{r} \$8.40 \\ \times 742 \\ \hline \end{array}$	19. $\begin{array}{r} \$22.53 \\ \times 34 \\ \hline \end{array}$	20. $\begin{array}{r} \$19.95 \\ \times 96 \\ \hline \end{array}$

21. $27 \times \$3.39 =$ _____ 22. $16 \times \$6.59 =$ _____

23. $20 \times \$9.54 =$ _____ 24. $32 \times \$9.08 =$ _____

25. $27 \times \$6.95 =$ _____ 26. $43 \times \$5.69 =$ _____

27. $418 \times \$2.54 =$ _____ 28. $673 \times \$4.04 =$ _____

Solve.

29. A dozen roses cost $12.95. How much would 6 dozen roses cost?

_____

30. A Swedish ivy plant costs $5.98. How much would 14 plants cost?

_____

Practice

Student Book pp. 100–101

4-1

If 5 friends share 40 apples, how many apples does each person have? To solve the problem, divide 40 by 5.

Remember. Division is the opposite of multiplication. If you know that $8 \times 5 = 40$ then $40 \div 5 = 8$.

Each person has 8 apples.

Division can be written in 2 ways.

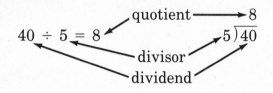

Divide.

1. $42 \div 7 = $ ____   **2.** $35 \div 5 = $ ____   **3.** $56 \div 7 = $ ____   **4.** $0 \div 4 = $ ____

5. $56 \div 8 = $ ____   **6.** $81 \div 9 = $ ____   **7.** $18 \div 3 = $ ____   **8.** $21 \div 3 = $ ____

9. $27 \div 3 = $ ____   **10.** $42 \div 7 = $ ____   **11.** $36 \div 9 = $ ____   **12.** $36 \div 6 = $ ____

13. $72 \div 9 = $ ____   **14.** $32 \div 8 = $ ____   **15.** $48 \div 8 = $ ____   **16.** $18 \div 9 = $ ____

17. $6\overline{)24}$ **18.** $5\overline{)25}$ **19.** $4\overline{)32}$ **20.** $7\overline{)35}$ **21.** $6\overline{)42}$

22. $9\overline{)72}$ **23.** $8\overline{)56}$ **24.** $3\overline{)27}$ **25.** $2\overline{)18}$ **26.** $4\overline{)16}$

27. $5\overline{)40}$ **28.** $6\overline{)54}$ **29.** $7\overline{)49}$ **30.** $8\overline{)32}$ **31.** $2\overline{)10}$

Use the opposites property to solve.

32. $8 \times 2 = 16$ **33.** $9 \times 4 = 36$ **34.** $5 \times 9 = 45$
so $16 \div 2 = n$ so $36 \div 4 = n$ so $45 \div n = 5$

_____   _____   _____

Divide and check.

1. $3\overline{)22}$ 2. $5\overline{)13}$ 3. $7\overline{)46}$ 4. $4\overline{)23}$

5. $8\overline{)29}$ 6. $8\overline{)38}$ 7. $6\overline{)58}$ 8. $5\overline{)38}$

9. $3\overline{)14}$ 10. $9\overline{)35}$ 11. $6\overline{)25}$ 12. $9\overline{)77}$

13. $4\overline{)13}$ 14. $7\overline{)69}$ 15. $5\overline{)31}$ 16. $7\overline{)60}$

17. $9\overline{)65}$ 18. $6\overline{)31}$ 19. $3\overline{)19}$ 20. $8\overline{)28}$

Solve.

21. The high school band is traveling to an away game in cars. How many cars are needed, if there are 45 band members and each car holds 5 members? _____

22. Wendy is supposed to practice a certain scale on her flute 28 minutes a week. How many minutes a day is this? _____

Practice

Student Book pp. 104–105

Sometimes when you divide, you need to work in two stages.
Let's divide 409 by 5.

First

Think of
5)40.

Subtract
8 × 5.

$$\begin{array}{r} 8 \\ 5\overline{)409} \\ -40 \\ \hline 0 \end{array}$$

Second

Think of
5)9.

Subtract
1 × 5.

$$\begin{array}{r} 81\ R4 \\ 5\overline{)409} \\ -40 \\ \hline 9 \\ -5 \\ \hline 4 \end{array}$$

Divide and check.

1. 2)48

2. 4)88

3. 7)568

4. 6)369

5. 8)649

6. 9)459

7. 7)429

8. 6)368

9. 8)249

10. 5)57

11. 4)87

12. 3)68

Solve.

13. Joe had 157 extra baseball cards.
He gave them to 4 friends to share
equally. How many did each
person get? _____ How many
were left? ____

14. Jeff had 227 cards. He gave them
to his 3 brothers to share equally.
How many did each boy get? _____
How many were left? ____

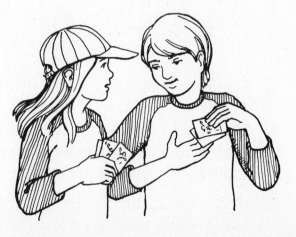

Practice
Student Book pp. 106–107

4-4

1. Match each problem with its correct quotient.

$8\overline{)310}$ | 37 R1 | $3\overline{)112}$

$5\overline{)186}$ | 46 R5 | $6\overline{)356}$

$9\overline{)419}$ | 38 R6 | $8\overline{)373}$

$6\overline{)339}$ | 59 R2 | $4\overline{)227}$

$4\overline{)238}$ | 46 R4 | $7\overline{)272}$

$7\overline{)326}$ | 56 R3 | $5\overline{)234}$

$4\overline{)384}$

2. Complete the problems to continue the sequence.

$3\overline{)48}^{\,16}$ $3\overline{)51}$ $3\overline{)}^{\,18}$ $3\overline{)}$ $\overline{)}$

$6\overline{)109}^{\,\text{R1}}$ $6\overline{)110}^{\,18\,\text{R2}}$ $6\overline{)}^{\,18\,\text{R3}}$ $6\overline{)}$ $\overline{)}$

$4\overline{)192}^{\,48}$ $4\overline{)194}^{\,48\,\text{R2}}$ $4\overline{)196}$ $4\overline{)}$ $\overline{)}$

Practice

Divide.

1. $7 \overline{)\$.49}$ **2.** $8 \overline{)\$.96}$ **3.** $3 \overline{)\$.84}$ **4.** $2 \overline{)\$.78}$ **5.** $5 \overline{)\$.45}$

6. $4 \overline{)\$3.44}$ **7.** $7 \overline{)\$2.45}$ **8.** $6 \overline{)\$4.08}$ **9.** $8 \overline{)\$4.24}$ **10.** $9 \overline{)\$5.67}$

11. $\$6.56 \div 8 =$ _____   **12.** $\$2.82 \div 3 =$ _____   **13.** $\$4.85 \div 5 =$ _____

Solve.

14. If tickets to a fair cost $3.75 each, what do 8 tickets cost?

_____

15. If 7 tickets for the ferris wheel cost $6.65, how much does each ticket cost? _____

16. On Saturday, the fair sold $768.75 worth of tickets. If Sunday's ticket sales totaled $682.50, how much more money was collected on Saturday? _____

Practice

4-6

Jan is in charge of planning an ice skating party. There is $48 in her club's treasury. The club wants to save $25. How much money can Jan spend on the party?

First decide whether to add, subtract, multiply, or divide.

The total amount available is $48, of which $25 cannot be spent. Subtract. $48 − $25 = $23. Jan can spend $23 on the party.

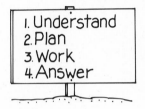

1. Understand
2. Plan
3. Work
4. Answer

Write *add*, *subtract*, *multiply*, or *divide*. Solve.

1. John spent $2.75 for his admission to the rink, $1.25 for skate rental, and $1.95 in the skate shop. How much did he spend altogether? _____

2. The skating rink pays its workers $4 an hour. Melissa earned $68 in one week. How many hours did she work? _____

3. The 6 workers in the skate shop work a total of 96 hours each week. If everyone works the same number of hours, how many hours does each one work? _____

4. After skating, 6 club members decided to have their skates sharpened. How much did it cost altogether? _____

5. Charlene bought 1 pair of skate protectors and 1 set of pom-poms. How much did she spend altogether? _____

6. Fran spent $10.90 in the skate shop. She bought leg warmers and something else. What else did she buy? _____

SKATE SHOP
Skates sharpened $3.50
Skate Protectors $1.95/pair
Leg Warmers $8.95
Pom-Poms $1.75/pair

Practice

Student Book pp. 112–113

Margarita packs 8 computer games in each box. If she has to pack 2740 games, how many complete boxes will she fill?

To solve, divide 2740 by 8.

Think $8\overline{)27}$.

$$
\begin{array}{r}
3 \\
8\overline{)2740} \\
-24 \\
\hline
3
\end{array}
$$

Think $8\overline{)34}$.

$$
\begin{array}{r}
34 \\
8\overline{)2740} \\
-24 \\
\hline
34 \\
-32 \\
\hline
2
\end{array}
$$

Think $8\overline{)20}$.

$$
\begin{array}{r}
342 \text{ R}4 \\
8\overline{)2740} \\
-24 \\
\hline
34 \\
-32 \\
\hline
20 \\
-16 \\
\hline
4
\end{array}
$$

Margarita will fill 342 complete boxes.

Divide.

1. $4\overline{)2865}$

2. $6\overline{)3272}$

3. $5\overline{)3666}$

4. $6\overline{)3858}$

5. $3\overline{)1919}$

6. $8\overline{)1839}$

7. $9\overline{)2964}$

8. $5\overline{)963}$

9. $4\overline{)934}$

10. $7\overline{)4023}$

Solve.

11. There are 2184 seats in the auditorium. There are 7 seats in each row. How many rows are there? _____

Practice

Student Book pp. 114–115

The winning team in the school jump-a-thon jumped 1624 times. There are 4 students on the team. How many times did each student jump?

Divide 1624 by 4.

Think of $4\overline{)16}$.

$$\begin{array}{r} 4 \\ 4\overline{)1624} \\ -16 \\ \hline 0 \end{array}$$

Think of $4\overline{)2}$.

$$\begin{array}{r} 40 \\ 4\overline{)1624} \\ -16 \\ \hline 2 \\ -0 \\ \hline 2 \end{array}$$

Think of $4\overline{)24}$.

$$\begin{array}{r} 406 \\ 4\overline{)1624} \\ -16 \\ \hline 2 \\ -0 \\ \hline 24 \\ -24 \\ \hline 0 \end{array}$$

Each student jumped 406 times.

Divide.

1. $5\overline{)1534}$

2. $4\overline{)821}$

3. $3\overline{)926}$

4. $6\overline{)3654}$

5. $7\overline{)802}$

6. $8\overline{)1674}$

7. $9\overline{)7605}$

8. $5\overline{)2402}$

9. $4\overline{)1239}$

10. $5\overline{)3926}$

11. $6\overline{)4020}$

12. $7\overline{)4203}$

Solve.

13. There were 424 children who took part in the jump-a-thon. If there were 4 children on each team, how many teams were there? _____

Practice
Student Book pp. 116–117

Solve.

1. Mr. Keller's class is going on a field trip. Each car can carry 5 students. If there are 38 students, how many cars are needed?

_____

2. The 38 students will be sitting in rows in an auditorium. If each row holds 8 people, how many rows are needed to seat the students?

_____

3. Mr. Keller divides the students into 7 groups. He wants to give each group an equal number of display items. If he has 25 items, how many can he give to each group?

_____

4. Mr. Keller has 140 pieces of drawing paper. How many pieces can each of the 38 students have for the project?

_____

5. The leader spent $39.61 on the class materials. How much money was spent on each of the 7 groups?

_____

6. Mr. Keller has 200 pieces of felt. How many pieces should he give to each of the 7 groups?

_____

7. The class will go on a special tour. There will be one guide for every 7 students. How many guides will be needed?

_____

8. The class stops at a restaurant on the way home. There are 110 chairs in this restaurant. How many tables of 4 are there?

_____

Practice

Mike is packing 415 dinner plates into cartons. If each carton holds 50 plates, how many complete cartons will be filled?

To find out, you divide.

Think of $5\overline{)41}$.

$$\begin{array}{r} 8 \text{ R}15 \\ 50\overline{)415} \\ -\ 400 \\ \hline 15 \end{array}$$

8 cartons will be completely filled.

Divide.

1. $10\overline{)39}$ **2.** $10\overline{)43}$ **3.** $20\overline{)195}$ **4.** $30\overline{)254}$

5. $50\overline{)236}$ **6.** $40\overline{)184}$ **7.** $30\overline{)196}$ **8.** $50\overline{)420}$

9. $40\overline{)350}$ **10.** $20\overline{)186}$ **11.** $40\overline{)252}$ **12.** $50\overline{)435}$

13. $70\overline{)563}$ **14.** $80\overline{)424}$ **15.** $60\overline{)420}$ **16.** $70\overline{)352}$

17. $90\overline{)281}$ **18.** $70\overline{)508}$ **19.** $90\overline{)641}$ **20.** $60\overline{)485}$

21. $\$286 \div 70 = $ _____ **22.** $450 \div 90 = $ _____ **23.** $562 \div 80 = $ _____

Solve.

24. The total cost of a school trip is $480. If 60 students are going on the trip, what is the cost per student? _____

Divide 452 by 46.

Round 46 up to 50.

Think of $5\overline{)45}$.

$$50 \circ\circ\circ \quad {}^{9}\!\!46\overline{)452}$$

Complete the division.

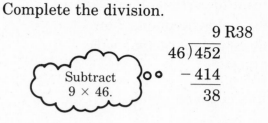

$$\begin{array}{r} 9\text{ R}38 \\ 46\overline{)452} \\ -414 \\ \hline 38 \end{array}$$

Subtract 9×46.

Divide.

1. $17\overline{)45}$ **2.** $19\overline{)88}$ **3.** $58\overline{)183}$ **4.** $67\overline{)215}$

5. $46\overline{)450}$ **6.** $79\overline{)251}$ **7.** $58\overline{)423}$ **8.** $68\overline{)220}$

9. $26\overline{)94}$ **10.** $45\overline{)250}$ **11.** $37\overline{)163}$ **12.** $65\overline{)212}$

13. $126 \div 36 =$ _____ **14.** $324 \div 77 =$ _____ **15.** $215 \div 28 =$ _____

16. $\$1.48 \div 37 =$ _____ **17.** $\$2.88 \div 48 =$ _____ **18.** $\$378 \div 54 =$ _____

Solve.

19. Roberta uses 27 inches of material to make an apron. If she has 234 inches of material, how many aprons can she make? _____

Practice

5-3

Divide. Then add the quotients of each pair of problems.
(Do not include the remainders.)

1. $12\overline{)99}$	**2.** $75 \div 15 =$ ___	**3.** $13\overline{)27}$	**4.** $96 \div 24 =$ ___
5. $56\overline{)168}$	**6.** $216 \div 36 =$ ___	**7.** $51\overline{)462}$	**8.** $182 \div 26 =$ ___
___ + ___ = $\bigcirc$	___ + ___ = $\bigcirc$	___ + ___ = $\bigcirc$	___ + ___ = $\bigcirc$

What number is in every circle? _____

9. $83\overline{)761}$	**10.** $156 \div 39 =$ ___	**11.** $75\overline{)594}$	**12.** $276 \div 46 =$ ___
13. $48\overline{)180}$	**14.** $584 \div 73 =$ ___	**15.** $54\overline{)270}$	**16.** $162 \div 27 =$ ___
___ + ___ = $\bigcirc$	___ + ___ = $\bigcirc$	___ + ___ = $\bigcirc$	___ + ___ = $\bigcirc$

What number is in every circle? _____

Practice

Student Book pp. 132–133

The Ruiz family is going to Florida for a vacation. They have decided to drive the 2400 kilometers instead of flying. The total cost for the family to drive round-trip will be $600. The round-trip airfare is $189 per person. There are 4 people in the Ruiz family. How much will they save by driving?

You need to follow two steps to solve this problem.

Step 1	**Step 2**
Find the cost of round-trip airfare for 4 people.	Find how much more the cost of airfare is than the cost of driving.
$189 × 4 ——— $756	$756 − 600 ——— $156

The Ruiz family saves $156 by driving to Florida.

Solve.

1. The car can be driven 400 km on a full tank of gas. If a full tank of gas costs $19, what will be the cost of gas for a 2400 km trip? _____

2. Mr. Ruiz plans to spend four days on the road. He will drive 700 km each day during the first three days. If the entire trip is 2400 km, how many kilometers will he have left to drive on the fourth day? _____

3. Along the way, the family will spend three nights in a motel. Mrs. Ruiz has already made two of the reservations. The first motel will cost $58, and the second one will cost $62. Mrs. Ruiz does not want to spend more than $175 altogether on the three motels. What is the most that the third motel can cost? _____

4. Mr. and Mrs. Ruiz want to spend no more than $1200 for the entire vacation. They will spend 5 days in Florida. The hotel they will stay at costs $54 a day. Their round-trip traveling expenses are $600. How much do they have left to spend on other expenses during their vacation? _____

Divide 712 by 17. You can round the divisor each time you need to estimate a digit in the quotient.

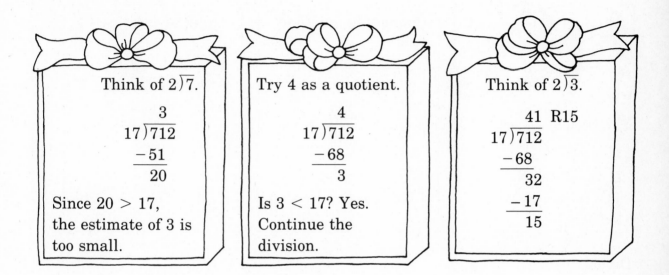

Think of $2\overline{)7}$.

$$\begin{array}{r} 3 \\ 17\overline{)712} \\ -51 \\ \hline 20 \end{array}$$

Since 20 > 17, the estimate of 3 is too small.

Try 4 as a quotient.

$$\begin{array}{r} 4 \\ 17\overline{)712} \\ -68 \\ \hline 3 \end{array}$$

Is 3 < 17? Yes. Continue the division.

Think of $2\overline{)3}$.

$$\begin{array}{r} 41 \ \ R15 \\ 17\overline{)712} \\ -68 \\ \hline 32 \\ -17 \\ \hline 15 \end{array}$$

Divide. Make sure that the remainder at each stage is less than the divisor.

1. $16\overline{)499}$ **2.** $27\overline{)895}$ **3.** $23\overline{)969}$ **4.** $36\overline{)\$9.00}$

5. $42\overline{)983}$ **6.** $57\overline{)912}$ **7.** $31\overline{)750}$ **8.** $49\overline{)995}$

9. $72\overline{)868}$ **10.** $86\overline{)920}$ **11.** $94\overline{)952}$ **12.** $34\overline{)904}$

13. $\$6.90 \div 46 = $ _____ **14.** $\$9.96 \div 83 = $ _____ **15.** $\$9.36 \div 72 = $ _____

Solve.

16. Mrs. Gilbert has 432 pencils to give to the students in her class. If there are 36 students, how many pencils can she give to each student? _____

Practice

5-6

Divide 1526 by 36.

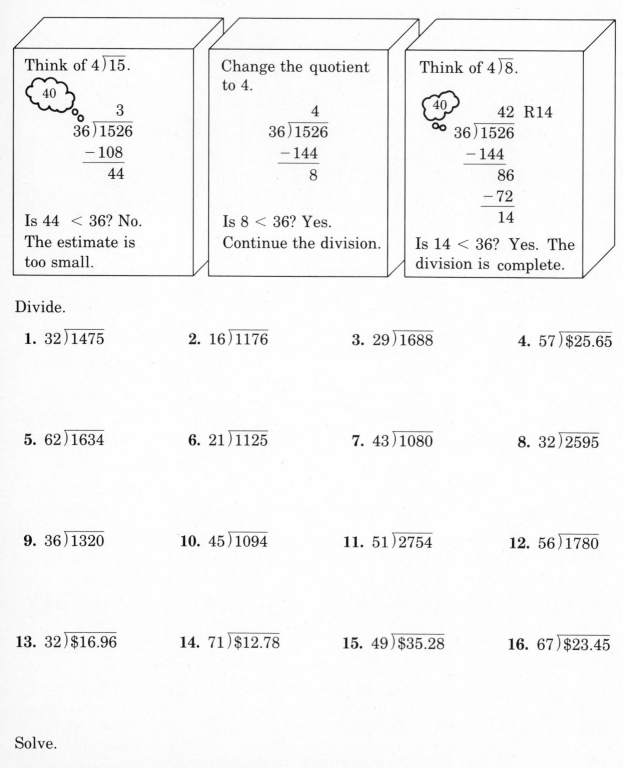

Think of $4\overline{)15}$.	Change the quotient to 4.	Think of $4\overline{)8}$.

Is 44 < 36? No. The estimate is too small.

Is 8 < 36? Yes. Continue the division.

Is 14 < 36? Yes. The division is complete.

Divide.

1. $32\overline{)1475}$ **2.** $16\overline{)1176}$ **3.** $29\overline{)1688}$ **4.** $57\overline{)\$25.65}$

5. $62\overline{)1634}$ **6.** $21\overline{)1125}$ **7.** $43\overline{)1080}$ **8.** $32\overline{)2595}$

9. $36\overline{)1320}$ **10.** $45\overline{)1094}$ **11.** $51\overline{)2754}$ **12.** $56\overline{)1780}$

13. $32\overline{)\$16.96}$ **14.** $71\overline{)\$12.78}$ **15.** $49\overline{)\$35.28}$ **16.** $67\overline{)\$23.45}$

Solve.

17. Sara's father raised 1190 bushels of wheat on 35 acres of farmland. How many bushels were raised on each acre? _____

Practice

Student Book pp. 138–139

Divide.

1. $23\overline{)5803}$

2. $35\overline{)7364}$

3. $57\overline{)8253}$

4. $34\overline{)9641}$

5. $76\overline{)9894}$

6. $45\overline{)5940}$

7. $68\overline{)8729}$

8. $17\overline{)5680}$

9. $13\overline{)9638}$

10. $79\overline{)8961}$

11. $56\overline{)7197}$

12. $82\overline{)9862}$

Solve.

13. Wayne will travel round-trip from New York City to Los Angeles. He figures it is 9196 km. If he travels an average of 76 km per hour, how many hours will the trip take?

14. If Wayne could average 82 km per hour, how long would a 9348 km trip take?

Study these examples of front-end estimation.

Estimate 432 + 286 + 129 + 345.
   Think: 400 + 200 + 100 + 300 = 1000
   Then think: 32 + 86 is about 100.
   Then think: 29 + 45 is about 100.
   The sum is about 1200.

Estimate 634 − 278.
   Think: 600 − 200 = 400
   Then think: 78 > 34 so
   subtract 50 from 400.
   The difference is about 350.

Estimate 7 × 384.
   Think: 7 × 300 = 2100
   84 is about 100, and
   7 × 100 = 700.
   The product is about 2800.

Estimate 9243 ÷ 31.
   Think: 9000 ÷ 30 = 300
   The quotient is about 300.

Estimate using front-end estimation.

1. 3892
    4156
    2874
   +3192

2.   469
     348
     514
    +176

3. 7264
   −1892

4. $68.06
   − 47.39

5. 22$\overline{)6172}$

6. 3976
    ×9

7. 4818
    ×5

8. 80$\overline{)4286}$

Use front-end estimation to answer these questions: About how
much should the items cost? Is the amount of the bill
reasonable?

JOE'S HARDWARE STORE

9. screwdrivers   10. hammers

_____   _____

11. chisels   12. the total bill

_____   _____

3 screwdrivers	@ 3.15	$ 9.45
4 hammers	@ 9.75	39.00
4 chisels	@ 2.55	10.20
	total	$58.65

Practice

Student Book pp. 142–143

Tyrannosaurus Rex was the fiercest dinosaur that ever lived. This giant meat eater might eat 2087 pounds of meat in 31 days. About how much meat might a Tyrannosaurus Rex eat in 1 day?

Estimate the amount of meat eaten in 1 day. Estimate the quotient by using compatible numbers, or numbers that divide easily.

$$31\overline{)2087}$$

$$\begin{array}{r} 70 \\ 30\overline{)2100} \\ -2100 \end{array}$$

A Tyrannosaurus Rex might eat about 70 pounds of meat in 1 day.

Use compatible numbers to estimate the quotient.

1. $5\overline{)258}$

2. $9\overline{)267}$

3. $8\overline{)415}$

4. $47\overline{)348}$

5. $29\overline{)153}$

6. $78\overline{)558}$

7. $52\overline{)147}$

8. $19\overline{)138}$

9. $92\overline{)268}$

Estimate.

10. There are 296 students going on a school trip. If each bus holds 48 students, about how many buses are needed? _____

11. The students are going to take guided tours in groups. If there are 18 students in each group, about how many guides are needed? _____

Practice

Student Book pp. 152–153

Eight tenths are shaded.

Write the decimal as 0.8.
Read 0.8 as *eight tenths*.

  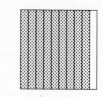

Three whole units and 9 tenths of a
whole unit are shaded.

Write the decimal as 3.9.
Read 3.9 as *three and nine tenths*.

Write the decimal.

1. 4 tenths _____

2. 5 tenths _____

3. 1 tenth _____

4. 6 and 3 tenths _____

5. 2 and 1 tenth _____

6. 7 and 5 tenths _____

7. 8 and 7 tenths _____

8. 6 and 4 tenths _____

9. 5 and 9 tenths _____

10. 23 and 5 tenths _____

11. 13 and 8 tenths _____

12. 34 and 6 tenths _____

13. 51 and 1 tenth _____

14. 45 and 7 tenths _____

15. 93 and 3 tenths _____

16. 6 hundreds 5 tens
    1 one and 6 tenths _____

17. 3 thousands and 9 tenths _____

18. 1 hundred 3 tens
    2 ones and 7 tenths _____

19. 6 thousands 2 tens
    5 ones and 4 tenths _____

20. two and four tenths _____

21. sixteen and three tenths _____

22. twenty-one and nine tenths _____

23. eighty-six and three tenths _____

24. four hundred ten
    and five tenths _____

25. five hundred
    and four tenths _____

Write the measurement using mathematical symbols.

26. The downhill ski racer finished the course in
    fifty-nine and two tenths seconds. _____

27. The high jump record for the day was two and
    one tenth meters. _____

28. The winning goal in the basketball game was
    scored with only three and seven tenths seconds
    left in the game. _____

Name _____

Practice
Student Book pp. 154–155
6-2

46 hundredths are shaded.

Write 0.46.
Read 0.46 as *forty-six hundredths*.

2 whole units and 7 parts are shaded.

Write 2.07.
Read 2.07 as *two and seven hundredths*.

Write the decimal.

1. 8 hundredths _____ **2.** 15 hundredths _____ **3.** 27 hundredths _____

4. 7 hundredths _____ **5.** 42 hundredths _____ **6.** 6 hundredths _____

7. 6 tenths and 3 hundredths _____ **8.** 9 tenths and 2 hundredths _____

9. 5 tenths and 4 hundredths _____ **10.** 7 tenths and 6 hundredths _____

11. 7 and 17 hundredths _____ **12.** 5 and 87 hundredths _____

13. 95 and 54 hundredths _____ **14.** 86 and 3 hundredths _____

15. 75 and 64 hundredths _____ **16.** 91 and 9 hundredths _____

17. 359 and 47 hundredths _____ **18.** 215 and 6 hundredths _____

19. 613 and 59 hundredths _____ **20.** 495 and 99 hundredths _____

21. thirty and fifteen hundredths _____ **22.** sixteen and one hundredth _____

23. fifty-three and sixteen hundredths _____

24. seven thousand and eighteen hundredths _____

One hundred cents make a dollar. Use this information to complete the following.

25. 36 cents = _____ hundredths of a dollar = _____

26. 8 cents = _____ hundredths of a dollar = _____

27. 235 cents = _____ and _____ hundredths of a dollar = _____

28. 672 cents = _____ and _____ hundredths of a dollar = _____

Practice

6-3

Write the value of each digit in the number 76.052.

tens	ones		tenths	hundredths	thousandths
7	6	.	0	5	2

You read 76.052 as *seventy-six and fifty-two thousandths*.
The value of the digit 7 is *7 tens*.
The value of the digit 6 is *6 ones*.
The value of the digit 0 is *0 tenths*.
The value of the digit 5 is *5 hundredths*.
The value of the digit 2 is *2 thousandths*.

Write the value of the underlined digit.

1. 5.4<u>4</u>8 _____

2. 4.78<u>3</u> _____

3. 8.3<u>7</u>5 _____

4. <u>9</u>.431 _____

5. 6.4<u>0</u>2 _____

6. 4.21<u>2</u> _____

7. 3<u>1</u>.296 _____

8. 27.<u>5</u>08 _____

9. 16.4<u>2</u>8 _____

Write as a decimal.

10. 36 thousandths _____

11. 8 thousandths _____

12. 535 thousandths _____

13. 52 thousandths _____

14. 2 and 12 thousandths _____

15. 13 and 272 thousandths _____

16. 24 and 75 thousandths _____

17. 65 and 8 thousandths _____

18. seven and two hundred twelve thousandths _____

19. thirty-four and fifteen thousandths _____

Who am I? Draw a line to match.

20. I have a four in my thousandths' place. Two of my digits are the same.   3.908

21. I have a nine in my tenths' place. I am less than four.   0.513

22. I have a one in my hundredths' place. I am less than one.   2.324

23. I have a zero in my ones' place and a zero in my tenths' place. I am less than one.   0.072

Practice

Student Book pp. 158–159

6-4

Write <, >, or =.

1. 6.37 ◯ 6.29

2. 25.07 ◯ 23.89

3. 426.76 ◯ 426.67

4. 39.2 ◯ 29.8

5. 148.386 ◯ 148.863

6. 2.047 ◯ 1.998

7. 761.502 ◯ 761.524

8. 3.86 ◯ 3.08

9. 17.006 ◯ 17.060

10. 83.563 ◯ 83.056

11. 208.001 ◯ 280.011

12. 70.5 ◯ 70.5

13. 384.587 ◯ 384.857

14. 29.687 ◯ 29.786

15. 327.94 ◯ 327.49

16. 5.006 ◯ 5.606

17. 98.805 ◯ 89.508

18. 706.397 ◯ 706.039

19. 63.36 ◯ 36.63

20. 407.206 ◯ 407.026

21. 96.374 ◯ 96.734

22. 526.831 ◯ 526.083

23. 7.567 ◯ 7.567

24. 43.896 ◯ 43.969

25. 5.040 ◯ 5.004

26. 390.007 ◯ 309.070

27. 27.604 ◯ 27.064

28. 316.20 ◯ 316.02

29. 94.221 ◯ 94.212

30. 8.43 ◯ 8.34

31. 17.051 ◯ 17.061

32. 9.4 ◯ 90.4

33. 2.076 ◯ 2.066

Write the decimals in order from least to greatest.

34. 5.66, 6.56, 4.56, 6.66

35. 0.08, 1.08, 0.18, 0.81

36. 13.00, 12.99, 13.01, 12.09

37. 4.609, 4.619, 4.019, 4.191

Rewrite the sentence, putting a decimal point in the number so that the sentence makes sense.

38. The family took 25 L of juice on the picnic.

39. The length of the desk is 1567 m.

40. The pitcher holds 245 L of water.

Practice

Student Book pp. 160–161

Compare 82.568 and 82.59.

tens	ones		tenths	hundredths	thousandths
8	2	.	5	6	8
8	2	.	5	9	0

same same   same   The hundredths are different.

6 hundredths < 9 hundredths

so 82.568 < 82.590

or 82.59 > 82.568

> Writing a zero after the last digit of a decimal does not change the value of the decimal.
>
> 82.59 = 82.590

Write <, >, or = to compare the decimals.

1. 0.3 _____ 0.24   **2.** 0.6 _____ 0.66   **3.** 1.5 _____ 1.48

4. 0.93 _____ 0.9   **5.** 4.5 _____ 4.51   **6.** 8.19 _____ 8.19

7. 4.09 _____ 4.1   **8.** 5.2 _____ 5.17   **9.** 6.3 _____ 6.29

10. 5.09 _____ 5.2   **11.** 9.06 _____ 9.6   **12.** 2.7 _____ 2.71

13. 3.35 _____ 3.4   **14.** 2.8 _____ 2.88   **15.** 12.3 _____ 12.29

16. 45.11 _____ 45.2   **17.** 36.31 _____ 36.29   **18.** 52.43 _____ 52.36

19. 0.87 _____ 0.087   **20.** 0.787 _____ 0.787   **21.** 6.501 _____ 6.05

22. 0.31 _____ 0.031   **23.** 3.512 _____ 3.51   **24.** 0.8 _____ 0.798

25. 5.06 _____ 5.600   **26.** 3.090 _____ 3.2   **27.** 5.102 _____ 4.939

Write the decimals in order from least to greatest.

28. 2.05, 1.15, 0.5, 0.55 _____

29. 14.06, 0.36, 6.86, 0.8 _____

30. 5.316, 3.518, 5.518, 4.618 _____

31. 5.02, 2.05, 5.2, 2.5 _____

32. 0.8, 1.08, 0.81, 0.081 _____

33. 3.5, 0.35, 30.5, 0.035 _____

34. 0.145, 41.6, 1.456, 6.14 _____

35. 78.3, 3.78, 370.8, 7.038 _____

36. 39.5, 9.5, 3.09, 5.93 _____

Practice

Student Book pp. 162–163

Name the coins. Use as many tries as you need in order to find the correct answer.

1. 3 coins that total $.40

2. 4 coins that total $.90

3. 4 coins that total $1.05

4. 7 coins that total $.53

5. 7 coins that total $.28

6. 5 coins that total $2.25

Solve.

7. You have 6 coins in your pocket. There are 2 of each kind of coin. The sum of the coins is $.80. What are the 6 coins?

8. The sporting goods store sold twice as many tennis racquets on Friday as on Thursday. There were 27 racquets sold during the 2 days. How many racquets were sold on each day?

9. Roberto bought a tennis racquet. He gave the salesman a fifty-dollar bill. Roberto's change was $6.00 less than he paid for the racquet. How much did he pay for the racquet?

10. Judy bought a hat, a sweater, and a tennis dress for a total of $28.50. The sweater was $3.50 more than the hat and the dress was $3.50 more than the sweater. How much did each item cost?

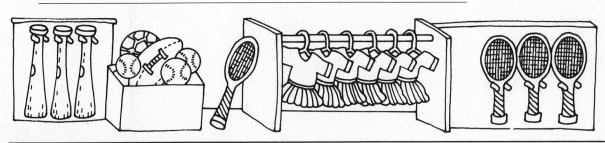

Practice
Student Book pp. 164–165

Round to the nearest hundredth.

1. 3.472 _____   **2.** 15.197 _____   **3.** 27.223 _____   **4.** 0.659 _____

5. 48.764 _____   **6.** 0.809 _____   **7.** 6.921 _____   **8.** 329.518 _____

Round to the nearest tenth.

9. 84.69 _____   **10.** 0.716 _____   **11.** 60.457 _____   **12.** 49.96 _____

13. 0.028 _____   **14.** 873.54 _____   **15.** 56.185 _____   **16.** 2.381 _____

Round to the nearest whole number.

17. 3.16 _____   **18.** 69.81 _____   **19.** 543.4 _____   **20.** 6.072 _____

21. 0.651 _____   **22.** 874.98 _____   **23.** 36.458 _____   **24.** 7.94 _____

Round to the place of the underlined digit.

25. 590.4 _____   **26.** 0.431 _____   **27.** 70.95 _____   **28.** 837.6 _____

29. 70.48 _____   **30.** 658.7 _____   **31.** 42.186 _____   **32.** 681.04 _____

Round to the nearest whole number, tenth, and hundredth.

33. 3.754 _____   **34.** 16.083 _____

35. 649.325 _____   **36.** 67.520 _____

Round each decimal to the place of the underlined digit.

37. Steve was surprised to find that the 83.573 mL of Giggle Juice he drank was good.

_____

38. Colleen threw away the Green Glop—all 77.06 mL of it!

_____

39. Amber had fun using the 106.993 mL of invisible ink.

_____

Practice
Student Book pp. 166–167

During one snowstorm, 45.7 cm of snow fell. The next day there was another snowstorm. This time 18.2 cm of snow fell. About how much snow fell in all?

To estimate, round each addend to its greatest place value. Then add the rounded numbers.

$$
\begin{array}{rcr}
45.7 & \longrightarrow & 50 \\
+\ 18.2 & \longrightarrow & +\ 20 \\
\hline
& & 70
\end{array}
$$

About 70 cm of snow fell in all.

Round to the greatest place value. Estimate the sum or difference.

1. 9.3
   +3.9

2. 7.8
   −6.4

3. 5.2
   −3.7

4. 56.7
   + 9.13

5. 25.04
   +25.19

6. 32.82
   + 9.10

7. 92.56
   −21.08

8. 103.09
   + 91.82

9. 79.19
   − 5.91

10. 83.5
   + 9.82

11. 99.19
   − 5.1

12. 99.85
   − 6.2

13. 5.19 + 4.89 _____

14. 19.2 − 8.79 _____

15. 252.81 − 113.05 _____

16. 6427.25 + 2873.9 _____

Round to the greatest place value. Estimate.

17. The Potter family drove 98.72 km in the morning and 56.3 km in the afternoon. About how many kilometers did they drive in all?

_____

In June, Jason was 153.25 cm tall. During the summer he grew 2.50 cm. How tall was he at the end of the summer?

To find out, add 153.25 and 2.50. When you add decimals, be sure to line up the decimal points.

```
  153.25
+   2.50
--------
  155.75
```

Jason was 155.75 cm tall at the end of the summer.

Add.

1. 0.6 + 0.2
2. 0.7 + 0.5
3. 7.4 + 0.1
4. 8.4 + 0.41
5. 6.7 + 1.45

6. 4.34 + 2.8
7. 0.312 + 0.82
8. 3.59 + 0.21
9. 12.45 + 2.16
10. 35.6 + 2.45

11. 15 + 2.45
12. 2.6 + 11.35
13. 3.95 + 0.246
14. 14.34 + 2.05
15. 12.04 + 3.02

16. 0.535 + 2.16
17. 12.03 + 2.004
18. 8.499 + 0.131
19. 136.25 + 0.54
20. 112.11 + 3.05

21. 27.3 + 4 = _____
22. 0.31 + 36.513 = _____
23. 3 + 0.4 + 0.51 = _____
24. 1.2 + 0.3 + 1.41 = _____

Solve.

25. Jason weighed 35.67 kg in June. During the summer, he gained 6.8 kg. How much did Jason weigh at the end of the summer? _____

26. Jason took 1.8 L of apple juice and 2.4 L of pineapple juice to a class picnic. How much juice did he take in all? _____

Practice

Student Book pp. 170–171

The pole vaulter won the event with a jump of 5.25 m. The second place vaulter jumped 4.80 m. How much higher did the first place vaulter jump than the second place vaulter?

Subtract 4.80 from 5.25. When you subtract decimals, always line up the decimal points.

$$\begin{array}{r} 5.25 \\ -4.80 \\ \hline 0.45 \end{array}$$

The first place pole vaulter jumped 0.45 m higher than the second place vaulter.

Subtract. Check by adding.

1.	2.	3.	4.	5.
4.33 −1.96	5.80 −1.94	4.394 −2.4	7.832 −3.915	4.763 −3.913

6.	7.	8.	9.	10.
8.9 −2.134	7.02 −3.199	5 −2.8	7.8 −1.9	16 −9.32

11.	12.	13.	14.	15.
58.37 −16.292	76.8 −21.49	92.134 −21.982	96.805 −12.6	79.1 −15.32

16.	17.	18.	19.	20.
86.3 −4.93	95 −10.2	86.3 −5.921	79.423 −25.34	86.12 −5.984

21. $15.9 - 6.32 =$ _____

22. $8 - 2.1 =$ _____

23. $5.38 - 0.9 =$ _____

24. $71.82 - 4.9 =$ _____

Solve.

25. The high jump record for the day was 2.30 m. Jim's best jump was 2.15 m. How much higher was the record jump than Jim's jump?

_____

Simplify the shopper's problem. Then solve.

"I need 1.5 kg of cheese. Each package weighs 0.5 kg. That means I need 3 packages. How much will that cost?" The shopper wants to know the price of 3 packages of cheese at $1.69 per package.

$$\begin{array}{r} \$1.69 \\ \times \quad 3 \\ \hline \$5.07 \end{array}$$

Three packages of cheese will cost $5.07.

Solve. Use easier numbers to help you if you need to. Use the supermarket prices above.

1. "I need a loaf of whole wheat bread and a package of muffins. How much will that cost?" _____

2. "I need 5 loaves of bread to make sandwiches for a class picnic. How much will 5 loaves of bread cost?" _____

3. "There are 4 people in my family. We each want a container of yogurt. How much will that cost?" _____

4. "I'm going to make cheese sandwiches. I need a loaf of bread and a package of cheese. How much will that cost?" _____

Use the list of store specials to answer these questions.

5. "How many rolls can I get for $1.19?" _____

6. "How many biscuits can I get for $.79?" _____

STORE SPECIALS	
1 dozen rolls	$1.19
$\frac{1}{2}$ dozen biscuits	$ .79
orange juice 0.75 L container	$ .89

7. "I need 24 rolls. That means I need 2 dozen. How much will that cost?"

_____

Estimate the product of 529.72 and 18.29.

Round both factors to the greatest place value.

$$
\begin{array}{rcr}
529.72 & \longrightarrow & 500 \\
\times\ 18.29 & \longrightarrow & \times\ 20 \\
\hline
& & 10,000
\end{array}
$$

The product of 529.72 and 18.29 is about 10,000.

Estimate the product.

1. 6.27
× 4.9

2. 5.8
× 3.7

3. 27.8
× 3.81

4. 432.3
× 7.6

5. 5.72
× 3.88

6. 18.5
× 8.6

7. 16.2
× 9.2

8. 620.8
× 6.2

9. 215.9
× 4.78

10. 87.2
× 8.3

11. 314.9
× 6.7

12. 597.2
× 6.8

13. 36.6
× 1.2

14. 79.2
× 2.5

15. 69.8
× 2.64

16. 297.1
× 632.9

17. 8.91×3.1 _____

18. 6.5×4.9 _____

19. 37.0×106.9 _____

20. 97.3×49.2 _____

21. 781.9×326.9 _____

22. 697.8×647.2 _____

Estimate to solve.

23. Max jogs 1.4 km each day. Marlene jogs 3.4 times as far. About how far does Marlene jog each day? _____

24. Tai jogs 2.5 times as far as Meg each week. If Meg jogs 8.5 km each week, how far does Tai jog? _____

Practice
Student Book pp. 184–185

When you multiply a decimal by a whole number, the product
will have the same number of decimal places as the decimal.

$$0.635 \leftarrow \text{three decimal places}$$
$$\times \quad 61$$
$$\overline{\quad 635}$$
$$\underline{38\ 100}$$
$$38.735 \leftarrow \text{three decimal places}$$

$$2.64 \leftarrow \text{two decimal places}$$
$$\times 3\ 14$$
$$\overline{10\ 56}$$
$$26\ 40$$
$$\underline{792\ 00}$$
$$828.96 \leftarrow \text{two decimal places}$$

Multiply.

1. 8.3 $\times\ 6$	**2.** 47.3 $\times\ 4$	**3.** 0.98 $\times\ 7$	**4.** 29.64 $\times\ 3$	**5.** 0.750 $\times\ 6$
6. 3.9 $\times 41$	**7.** 0.5 $\times 37$	**8.** 8.4 $\times 56$	**9.** 3.15 $\times\ 29$	**10.** 63.7 $\times\ 58$
11. 621.5 $\times\ 36$	**12.** 0.573 $\times\ 31$	**13.** 90.46 $\times\ 57$	**14.** 742.5 $\times\ 46$	**15.** 25.98 $\times\ 78$

16. $37 \times 4.2 =$ _____

17. $5 \times 4.96 =$ _____

18. $29 \times 3.8 =$ _____

19. $53 \times 79.8 =$ _____

Solve.

20. Angelo rides his bicycle at a speed
of 5 km/h. Ralph can ride his
bicycle 1.75 times as fast. How fast
does Ralph ride his bicycle? _____

Practice

Student Book pp. 186–187

7-3

When you multiply a decimal by a decimal, the number of decimal places in the product is the total number of decimal places in the factors.

$$
\begin{array}{r}
0.93 \leftarrow \text{two decimal places} \\
\times\ 0.2 \leftarrow \text{one decimal place} \\
\hline
0.186 \leftarrow \text{three decimal places}
\end{array}
$$

Multiply.

1. 8.6 ×6.2	**2.** 0.7 ×3.9	**3.** 3.4 ×5.8	**4.** 5.8 ×2.9	**5.** 1.9 ×7.3
6. 60.9 × 2.4	**7.** 7.15 × 3.6	**8.** 69.24 × 9.5	**9.** 80.3 × 1.8	**10.** 7.92 × 3.4
11. 3.64 × 2.5	**12.** 85.2 × 3.8	**13.** 9.15 × 4.3	**14.** 7.09 × 9.1	**15.** 69.2 × 5.9

16. 2.9 × 7.5 = _____

17. 8.6 × 9.8 = _____

18. 78.2 × 1.6 = _____

19. 6.21 × 2.4 = _____

20. 7.96 × 3.2 = _____

21. 6.15 × 2.4 = _____

Solve.

22. Rob the Robot does many household chores. He can wash the floor in 38.9 s. It takes him 3.1 times longer to wax the floor. How much time does it take to wax the floor?

_____

23. Rob the Robot can wash a car in 5.6 min. It takes him 6.4 times as long to polish a car. How long does it take him to polish a car?

_____

Practice

Student Book pp. 188–189

When you multiply decimals, you may need to write zeros in the product.

0.3 of 0.2
0.06

$$0.2 \leftarrow \text{one decimal place}$$
$$\times 0.3 \leftarrow \text{one decimal place}$$
$$\overline{0.06} \leftarrow \text{two decimal places}$$

Multiply.

1.	0.8 ×0.1	**2.**	0.2 ×0.4	**3.**	0.1 ×0.6	**4.**	0.3 ×0.2	**5.**	0.5 ×0.1
6.	3.4 ×0.2	**7.**	1.8 ×0.4	**8.**	0.11 × 0.5	**9.**	0.41 × 0.3	**10.**	0.19 × 1.3
11.	0.8 ×1.41	**12.**	1.6 ×0.02	**13.**	0.5 ×0.13	**14.**	1.4 ×0.05	**15.**	1.1 ×0.06
16.	1.5 ×0.02	**17.**	1.4 ×0.06	**18.**	1.8 ×0.05	**19.**	2.9 ×0.02	**20.**	0.12 × 0.3

21. $3.1 \times 0.2 =$ _____   **22.** $0.4 \times 0.1 =$ _____   **23.** $0.6 \times 1.1 =$ _____

24. $0.06 \times 0.2 =$ _____   **25.** $4.2 \times 0.03 =$ _____   **26.** $1.02 \times 0.6 =$ _____

Solve.

27. Kim ran 2.8 km on Saturday. She ran 0.2 times as far on Sunday. How far did she run on Sunday?

_____

28. Terry used 0.56 L of paint to paint a table. He used 0.3 times as much paint to paint a sign. How much paint did he use to paint the sign?

_____

Practice
Student Book pp. 190–191

Use the table of motel rates on the right to check whether the clerk's answers are reasonable. If an answer is reasonable, write *R*. If not, explain why not and find the correct answer.

DO-DROP-INN ROOM RATES	
1 person per room	$43.95
2 people - twin beds	$46.95
2 people - double beds	$45.95
3 people per room	$51.95
4 people per room	$53.95

1. You say "I need a room for tonight and tomorrow night." The clerk says, "It will cost you $59.90."

2. You ask "What would be the cost for two people to rent a room with double beds for two nights?" The clerk says, "It will cost $183.80."

3. You ask "How much will it cost for three people to rent one room for 3 nights?" The clerk says, "It will cost less than $150."

4. You ask "About how much will it cost for four people in one room for two nights?" The clerk says, "It will cost about $100."

5. You ask "How much will it cost for two people in a room with double beds for four nights?" The clerk says, "It will cost about $250.00."

Practice
Student Book pp. 192–193

Mrs. Chan bought 1.20 kg of meat to make hamburgers for 15 people. How much meat will be in each hamburger?

Divide 1.20 by 15. You will need to write zeros in the quotient to have the correct number of decimal places.

$$
\begin{array}{r}
0.08 \\
15\overline{)1.20} \\
-1\,20 \\
\hline
0
\end{array}
$$

Each hamburger will weigh 0.08 kg.

Divide.

1. $6\overline{)4.2}$

2. $9\overline{)2.7}$

3. $8\overline{)4.8}$

4. $9\overline{)7.2}$

5. $6\overline{)1.50}$

6. $8\overline{)14.4}$

7. $9\overline{)24.3}$

8. $7\overline{)16.1}$

9. $3\overline{)0.84}$

10. $7\overline{)18.9}$

11. $6\overline{)1.44}$

12. $5\overline{)21.5}$

13. $18\overline{)12.6}$

14. $23\overline{)1.61}$

15. $46\overline{)27.6}$

16. $37\overline{)2.96}$

17. $55\overline{)44.0}$

18. $76\overline{)6.84}$

19. $32\overline{)1.92}$

20. $17\overline{)13.6}$

21. $43.2 \div 54 = $ _____

22. $5.74 \div 82 = $ _____

23. $90.0 \div 36 = $ _____

Solve.

24. Mrs. Chan bought 6 packages of hamburger rolls for $7.74. How much did each package cost? _____

Practice
Student Book pp. 194–195

Four pirates found a treasure chest containing 297 g of gold. How many grams will each pirate get if they divide the treasure equally?

Divide 297 by 4.

```
        74.25
  4)297.00
   −28
    17
   − 16
     10
    − 8
     20
    − 20
      0
```

Each pirate will get 74.25 g of gold.

Divide.

1. $5\overline{)71.7}$ 2. $2\overline{)9.15}$ 3. $4\overline{)1.4}$ 4. $6\overline{)3.3}$ 5. $8\overline{)83.6}$

6. $5\overline{)13.7}$ 7. $4\overline{)38}$ 8. $2\overline{)7.9}$ 9. $25\overline{)615}$ 10. $32\overline{)81.6}$

11. $48\overline{)15.6}$ 12. $76\overline{)140.6}$ 13. $64\overline{)572.8}$ 14. $42\overline{)153.3}$ 15. $75\overline{)282}$

Solve.

16. The 4 pirates together weigh 291.2 kg. What is their average weight in kilograms? _____

Name _____

Which is longer?

rope ◀ 9.2 cm

rope ◀ 91 mm

To compare measurements, the units must be the same.

You can change 9.2 cm to mm.

To change cm to mm, you multiply by 10.

    9.2 cm   9.2 × 10   92 mm

    92 mm > 91 mm so the rope on the top is longer.

To change mm to cm you divide by 10.

    91 mm   91 ÷ 10   9.1 cm

When changing from a larger unit to a smaller unit, multiply.

When changing from a smaller unit to a larger unit, divide.

Change to millimeters.

1. 6.2 cm _____   **2.** 4.7 cm _____   **3.** 0.2 cm _____

4. 7.9 cm _____   **5.** 36.2 cm _____   **6.** 51.8 cm _____

7. 315.6 cm _____   **8.** 657.1 cm _____   **9.** 0.5 cm _____

Change to centimeters.

10. 6 mm _____   **11.** 8 mm _____   **12.** 16 mm _____

13. 31 mm _____   **14.** 37 mm _____   **15.** 456 mm _____

16. 709 mm _____   **17.** 146 mm _____   **18.** 253 mm _____

Write the missing number.

19. 6 km = _____ m   **20.** 8 km = _____ m   **21.** 54 km = _____ m

22. 3.7 km = _____ m   **23.** 7.7 km = _____ m   **24.** 9.2 km = _____ m

25. 2.65 km = _____ m   **26.** 3.48 km = _____ m   **27.** 6.53 km = _____ m

Which is greater? Circle your answer.

28. 31.6 cm or 310 mm   **29.** 55.2 cm or 560 mm

30. 21.9 cm or 225 mm   **31.** 75.8 cm or 710 mm

Practice

Solve by working backwards when necessary.

1. You want to be done with your homework by 8:30 P.M. You need to spend 45 min on Social Studies and 30 min on English. When should you begin your homework? _____

2. You want to arrive at the ball game by 2 P.M. It takes 45 min on the subway to get to the ballpark and takes 4 min to walk to the subway from your home. When should you leave home? _____

3. You want to be home from your vacation by August 6. On your vacation, you plan to spend 7 days visiting a friend and 10 days visiting your older brother. When should you plan to go on vacation? _____

4. You want to arrive at your grandparents' home for dinner at 6:00 P.M. It takes 30 min to get to the train station and buy your ticket. The train ride takes 45 min and it takes an additional 25 min to walk from the train station to your grandparents' home. When should you leave home to arrive on time? _____

5. You want to have $2.50 left after doing some shopping. You plan to buy a pen for $1.50 and 2 writing pads for 75¢ each. How much money do you need? _____

Practice

A rocket traveled 265.8 km in 28 s. About how many kilometers per second did the rocket travel?

$$28\overline{)266} \longrightarrow 30\overline{)300}$$
$$\begin{array}{r} 10 \\ 30\overline{)300} \\ -300 \\ \hline 0 \end{array}$$

The rocket traveled about 10 km per second.

Use compatible numbers to estimate the quotient.

1. $6\overline{)586.3}$

2. $5\overline{)299.5}$

3. $4\overline{)239.6}$

4. $3\overline{)588.2}$

5. $2\overline{)102.5}$

6. $7\overline{)678.9}$

7. $7\overline{)278.6}$

8. $5\overline{)347.9}$

9. $3\overline{)332.5}$

10. $8\overline{)635.9}$

11. $4\overline{)276.5}$

12. $9\overline{)815.4}$

13. $47\overline{)248.9}$

14. $74\overline{)493.8}$

15. $58\overline{)418.6}$

16. $28\overline{)207.5}$

17. $94\overline{)811.2}$

18. $22\overline{)436.5}$

Solve.

19. The spaceship Apollo 10 made 31 orbits in about 192.05 h. About how long did each orbit take? _____

Practice
Student Book pp. 210–211

8-1

Here are four geometric figures.

A ●————————● B	line *AB* or line *BA* written $\overleftrightarrow{AB}$ or $\overleftrightarrow{BA}$	A line has no endpoints. It goes on and on in both directions.
C ●————————● D	segment *CD* or segment *DC* written $\overline{CD}$ or $\overline{DC}$	A line segment is part of a line. It has two endpoints.
E ●————————● F	ray *EF* written $\overrightarrow{EF}$ (Always name the endpoint first.)	A ray is part of a line. It has one endpoint and goes on and on in one direction.
⟋ X ⟋	plane *X*	A plane is a flat surface that goes on and on in all directions.

Name the figure.

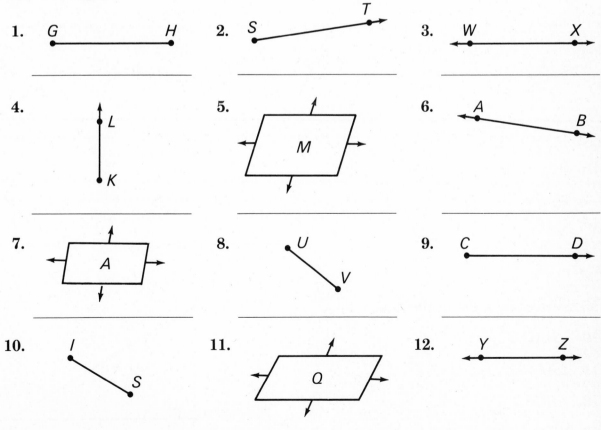

1. G ●————————● H

_____

2. S ●————————→ T

_____

3. W ●————————● X

_____

4. L ● ↑ | ● K

_____

5. M (plane)

_____

6. A ●————————● B

_____

7. A (plane)

_____

8. U ● ╲ ● V

_____

9. C ●————————● D

_____

10. I ● ╲ ● S

_____

11. Q (plane)

_____

12. Y ●————————● Z

_____

An **angle** is made up of two rays with a common endpoint. The common endpoint is the **vertex** of the angle. The angle is always named by using the letter of the vertex as the middle letter.

∠ABC or ∠CBA

∠DEF or ∠FED

We use a **protractor** to measure the size of an angle.
The unit for measuring angles is called a **degree.**

Angle *ABC* measures 60 degrees.
You write m∠*ABC* = 60°.

Angle *DEF* measures 110 degrees.
You write m∠*DEF* = 110°.

Measure the angle. Use a protractor.

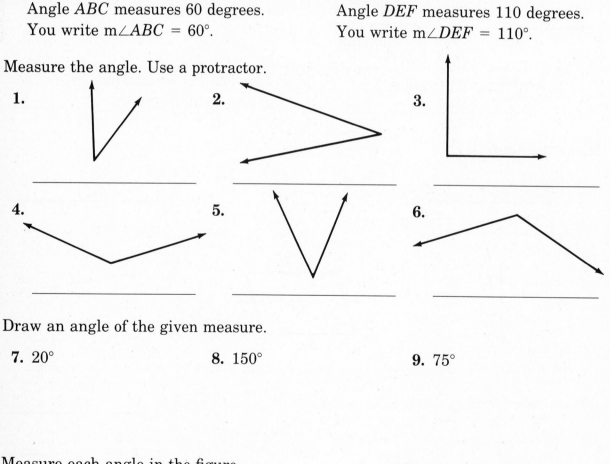

1. _____

2. _____

3. _____

4. _____

5. _____

6. _____

Draw an angle of the given measure.

7. 20°

8. 150°

9. 75°

Measure each angle in the figure.

10. ∠*BAC* _____

11. ∠*ABC* _____

12. ∠*BCA* _____

13. What is the sum of the 3 angles? _____

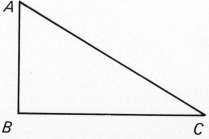

Name

A **right angle** measures 90°.	An **acute angle** measures less than 90°.	An **obtuse angle** measures more than 90°.
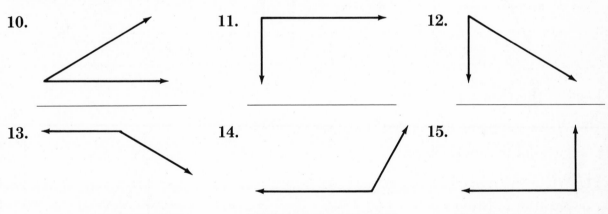		
Angle *ABC* measures 90°.	Angle *DEF* measures 40°.	Angle *PQR* measures 110°.

Write *acute, obtuse,* or *right* to describe the angle.

1. 35° _____   **2.** 88° _____   **3.** 90° _____

4. 115° _____   **5.** 25° _____   **6.** 170° _____

7. 55° _____   **8.** 92° _____   **9.** 115° _____

Estimate whether the angle is *acute, obtuse,* or *right.*

10. _____   **11.** _____   **12.** _____

13. _____   **14.** _____   **15.** _____

Look at the figure to the right.

16. Name four angles that look as if they are acute angles. _____

17. Name three angles that look as if they are obtuse angles. _____

18. Name two angles that look as if they are right angles. _____

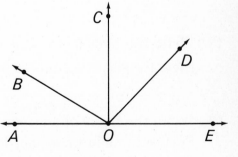

Practice

8-4

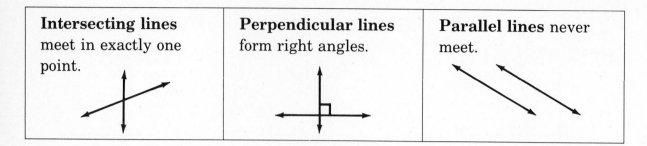

Intersecting lines meet in exactly one point.	**Perpendicular lines** form right angles.	**Parallel lines** never meet.

Write *intersecting, parallel,* or *perpendicular* to best describe the lines.

1. 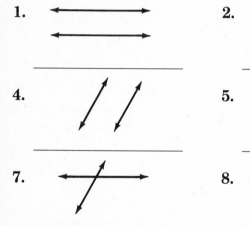 _____

2. _____

3. _____

4. _____

5. _____

6. _____

7. _____

8. _____

9. _____

Look at the road map.

10. Write the name of a street that looks as if it is parallel to Maple Street. _____

11. Write the name of a street that looks as if it is parallel to Birch Lane. _____

12. Write the names of two streets that look as if they are perpendicular to Willow Street.

_____

13. Write the names of two streets that look as if they are perpendicular to Maple Street.

_____

14. Write the name of a street that intersects Spruce Lane but does not look as if it is perpendicular to it. _____

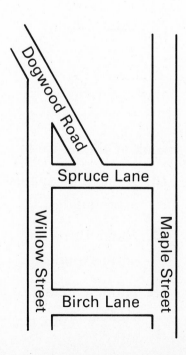

Practice
Student Book pp. 218–219

The point A is located by the ordered pair of numbers (3, 4). To get to A, start at 0, move 3 units to the right and then 4 units up.

Write the letter that is located at the ordered pair.

1. (3, 6) _____   **2.** (1, 8) _____   **3.** (4, 5) _____   **4.** (6, 2) _____

5. (6, 5) _____   **6.** (3, 7) _____   **7.** (6, 4) _____   **8.** (2, 5) _____

Write the letter for each ordered pair to spell a word.

9. $\underset{(6,\,4)}{\rule{2cm}{0.4pt}}$ $\underset{(3,\,4)}{\rule{2cm}{0.4pt}}$ $\underset{(2,\,5)}{\rule{2cm}{0.4pt}}$ $\underset{(3,\,7)}{\rule{2cm}{0.4pt}}$ $\underset{(8,\,1)}{\rule{2cm}{0.4pt}}$ $\underset{(4,\,5)}{\rule{2cm}{0.4pt}}$

10. $\underset{(2,\,5)}{\rule{2cm}{0.4pt}}$ $\underset{(6,\,2)}{\rule{2cm}{0.4pt}}$ $\underset{(1,\,8)}{\rule{2cm}{0.4pt}}$ $\underset{(8,\,4)}{\rule{2cm}{0.4pt}}$ $\underset{(3,\,4)}{\rule{2cm}{0.4pt}}$ $\underset{(4,\,5)}{\rule{2cm}{0.4pt}}$

11. $\underset{(3,\,6)}{\rule{2cm}{0.4pt}}$ $\underset{(8,\,8)}{\rule{2cm}{0.4pt}}$ $\underset{(3,\,7)}{\rule{2cm}{0.4pt}}$ $\underset{(1,\,8)}{\rule{2cm}{0.4pt}}$ $\underset{(3,\,3)}{\rule{2cm}{0.4pt}}$ $\underset{(2,\,5)}{\rule{2cm}{0.4pt}}$

Write the ordered pair for the letter.

12.   S   L   I   D   E   S

_____ _____ _____ _____ _____ _____

13.   A   U   G   U   S   T

_____ _____ _____ _____ _____ _____

14. Write a message using the grid as a secret code.

_____

_____

Practice

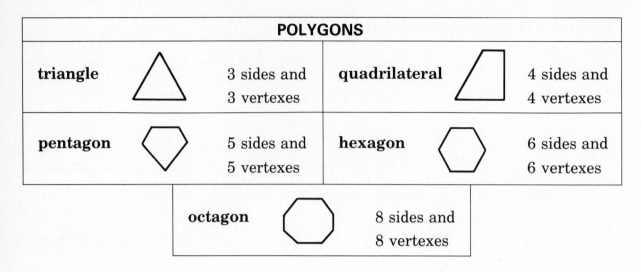

Write *triangle, quadrilateral, pentagon, hexagon,* or *octagon.*

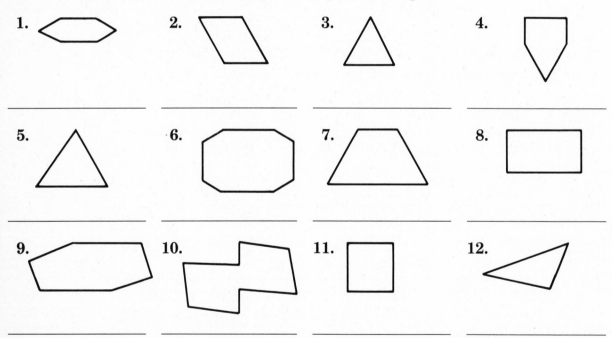

Draw a line to match.

13. a triangle with one obtuse angle

14. a hexagon with all sides the same length

15. a pentagon with all sides the same length

16. a figure with 8 vertexes

17. a figure with 4 vertexes

Name _____

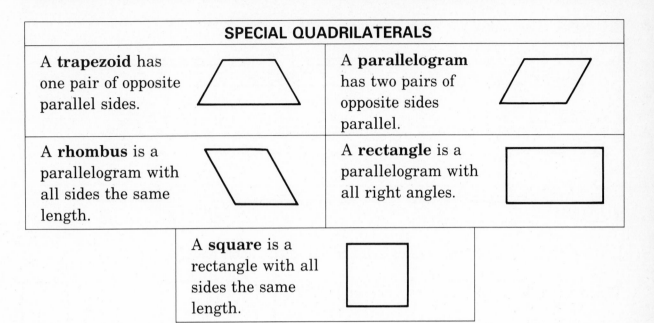

SPECIAL QUADRILATERALS	
A **trapezoid** has one pair of opposite parallel sides.	A **parallelogram** has two pairs of opposite sides parallel.
A **rhombus** is a parallelogram with all sides the same length.	A **rectangle** is a parallelogram with all right angles.
A **square** is a rectangle with all sides the same length.	

Use *trapezoid, parallelogram, rhombus, rectangle,* or *square* to best name the quadrilateral.

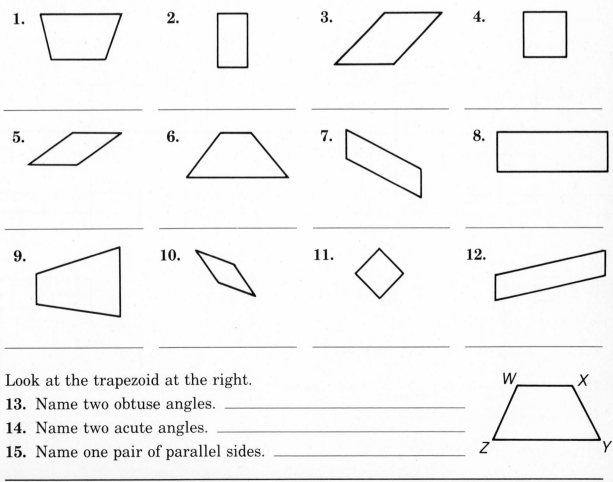

1. _____

2. _____

3. _____

4. _____

5. _____

6. _____

7. _____

8. _____

9. _____

10. _____

11. _____

12. _____

Look at the trapezoid at the right.

13. Name two obtuse angles. _____

14. Name two acute angles. _____

15. Name one pair of parallel sides. _____

Practice
Student Book pp. 224–225

Estimate. How many car lengths apart are the cars?

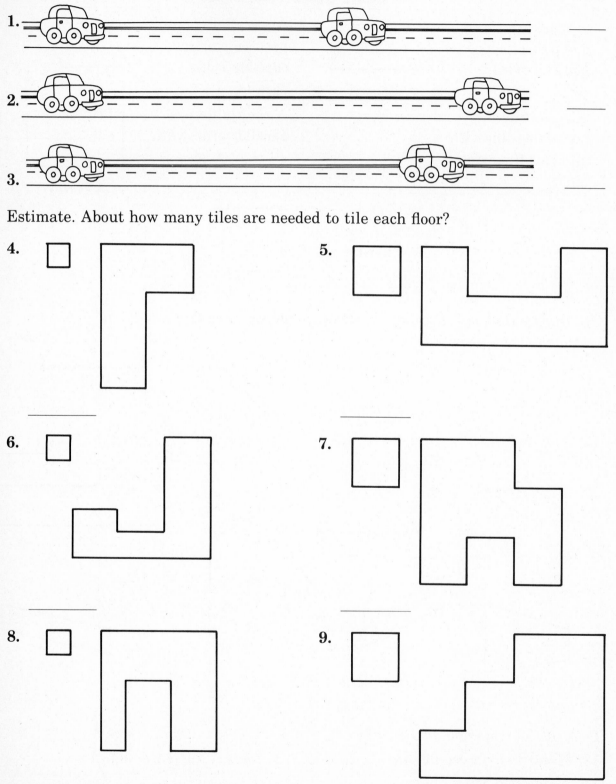

Estimate. About how many tiles are needed to tile each floor?

Name _____

How much fencing is needed to enclose a rectangular garden that measures 12 m by 15 m?

You must find the distance around the garden. This is called the **perimeter.**

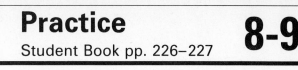

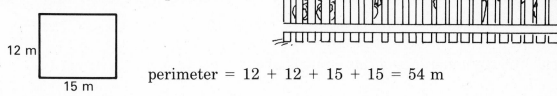

12 m

15 m

perimeter = 12 + 12 + 15 + 15 = 54 m

The perimeter of the garden is 54 m. You will need 54 m of fencing to enclose the garden.

What is the perimeter?

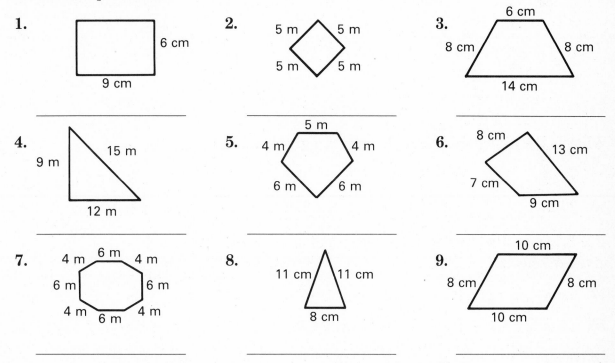

1.

6 cm

9 cm

_____

2.

5 m   5 m

5 m   5 m

_____

3.

6 cm

8 cm   8 cm

14 cm

_____

4.

9 m   15 m

12 m

_____

5.

5 m

4 m   4 m

6 m   6 m

_____

6.

8 cm   13 cm

7 cm

9 cm

_____

7.

4 m   6 m   4 m

6 m   6 m

4 m   6 m   4 m

_____

8.

11 cm   11 cm

8 cm

_____

9.

10 cm

8 cm   8 cm

10 cm

_____

Use mental math to find the perimeter of the figure. Look for combinations of 10 to make adding easier.

10. 5 cm, 9 cm, 5 cm _____

11. 15 mm, 12 mm, 8 mm _____

12. 6 cm, 7 cm, 14 cm, 13 cm _____

13. 16 m, 10 m, 24 m, 30 m _____

14. 14 mm, 12 mm, 28 mm, 6 mm _____

15. 35 cm, 22 cm, 15 cm, 18 cm _____

Name

Practice 8-10

Student Book pp. 228–229

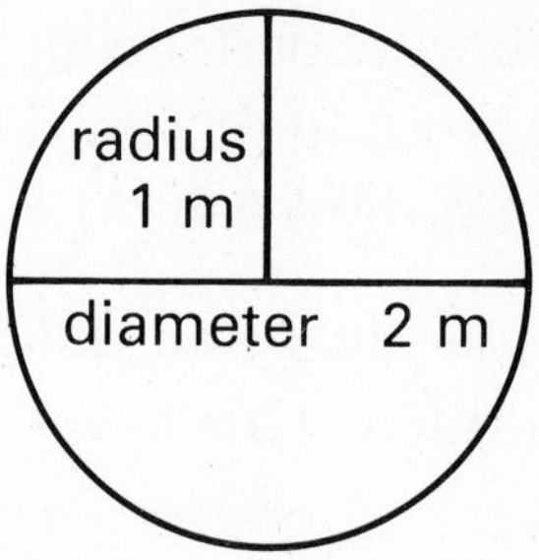

The distance from the center of a circle to any point on the circle is called the **radius.** The radius of this circle is 1 m.

The distance across a circle through the center is called the **diameter.** The diameter is twice the radius. The diameter of this circle is 2 m.

The distance around a circle is called the **circumference.** The circumference is a little more than 3.14 times the diameter of a circle. The circumference of this circle is about 6.28 m.

Draw a circle with the given radius.

1. 2 cm　　**2.** 14 mm　　**3.** 1.2 cm

What is the diameter of a circle with the given radius?

4. 7 cm ______　**5.** 5 cm ______　**6.** 8 cm ______　**7.** 6 cm ______

8. 20 m ______　**9.** 50 m ______　**10.** 11 cm ______　**11.** 100 m ______

Use 3.14 to estimate the circumference of a circle with the given diameter.

12. 6 cm ________　**13.** 5 m ________　**14.** 7 cm ________

15. 14 m ________　**16.** 4 cm ________　**17.** 9 m ________

18. 30 cm ________　**19.** 40 m ________　**20.** 13 cm ________

Look at the picture at the right.

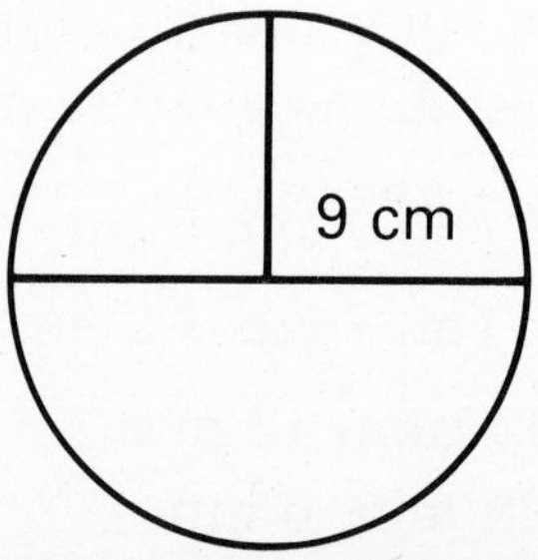

21. What is the radius of the circle? ________

22. What is the diameter of the circle? ________

23. Use 3.14 to estimate the circumference of the circle. ________

Name

The **area** of a shape is the number of square units that fit inside. A **square centimeter** (cm^2) is a common unit for measuring area. Each small square in the grid to the right is one square centimeter.

The area of this figure is 12 cm^2.

What is the area?

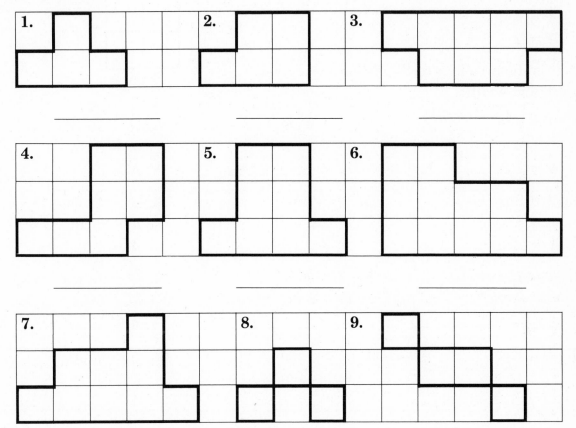

1. _____

2. _____

3. _____

4. _____

5. _____

6. _____

7. _____

8. _____

9. _____

Estimate the area of each drawing in square centimeters. Mentally piece together partially covered squares to make about one covered square.

10.

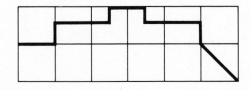

11.

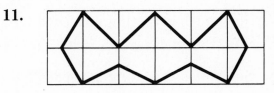

_____

_____

Name _____

Practice

Student Book pp. 232–233 **8-12**

To find the area (A) of a rectangle, multiply the length (l) by the width (w).

$A = l \times w$
$A = 4 \times 3$
$A = 12 \text{ cm}^2$

To find the area of a square, multiply a side (s) by itself.

$A = s \times s$
$A = 2 \times 2 = 4 \text{ cm}^2$

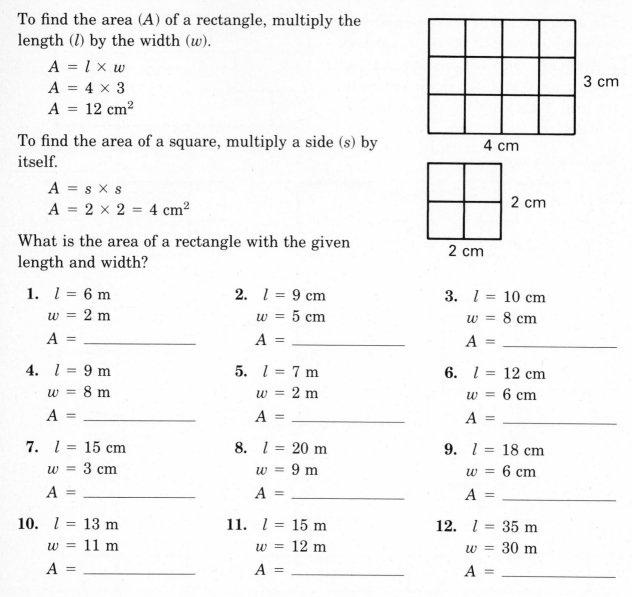

3 cm

4 cm

2 cm

2 cm

What is the area of a rectangle with the given length and width?

1. $l = 6$ m
   $w = 2$ m
   $A =$ _____

2. $l = 9$ cm
   $w = 5$ cm
   $A =$ _____

3. $l = 10$ cm
   $w = 8$ cm
   $A =$ _____

4. $l = 9$ m
   $w = 8$ m
   $A =$ _____

5. $l = 7$ m
   $w = 2$ m
   $A =$ _____

6. $l = 12$ cm
   $w = 6$ cm
   $A =$ _____

7. $l = 15$ cm
   $w = 3$ cm
   $A =$ _____

8. $l = 20$ m
   $w = 9$ m
   $A =$ _____

9. $l = 18$ cm
   $w = 6$ cm
   $A =$ _____

10. $l = 13$ m
    $w = 11$ m
    $A =$ _____

11. $l = 15$ m
    $w = 12$ m
    $A =$ _____

12. $l = 35$ m
    $w = 30$ m
    $A =$ _____

What is the area of a square with sides of the given length?

13. $s = 19$ cm
    $A =$ _____

14. $s = 28$ mm
    $A =$ _____

15. $s = 36$ m
    $A =$ _____

16. $s = 30$ cm
    $A =$ _____

Solve.

17. How much carpeting is needed for a rectangular room that measures 5 m by 3 m? _____

18. How much carpeting is needed for a rectangular room that measures 4 m by 4 m? _____

Practice

The area of a right triangle is half the area of a rectangle.

To find the area of a right triangle, first multiply the base (b) by the height (h). Then divide the product by 2.

$$A = (b \times h) \div 2 \qquad A = 32 \div 2$$
$$A = (8 \times 4) \div 2 \qquad A = 16 \text{ m}^2$$

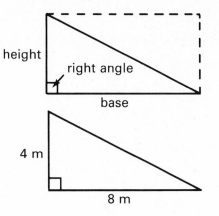

What is the area of a right triangle with the given base and height?

1. $b = 8$ cm
   $h = 5$ cm
   $A = $ _____

2. $b = 10$ m
   $h = 5$ m
   $A = $ _____

3. $b = 12$ cm
   $h = 7$ cm
   $A = $ _____

4. $b = 19$ cm
   $h = 14$ cm
   $A = $ _____

5. $b = 18$ m
   $h = 26$ m
   $A = $ _____

6. $b = 10$ m
   $h = 13$ m
   $A = $ _____

7. $b = 15$ cm
   $h = 42$ cm
   $A = $ _____

8. $b = 15$ cm
   $h = 10$ cm
   $A = $ _____

9. $b = 12$ cm
   $h = 33$ cm
   $A = $ _____

10. $b = 20$ m
    $h = 20$ m
    $A = $ _____

11. $b = 20$ m
    $h = 16$ m
    $A = $ _____

12. $b = 11$ m
    $h = 34$ m
    $A = $ _____

13. $b = 30$ cm
    $h = 10$ cm
    $A = $ _____

14. $b = 30$ m
    $h = 24$ m
    $A = $ _____

15. $b = 25$ cm
    $h = 14$ cm
    $A = $ _____

16. $b = 40.8$ cm
    $h = 10$ cm
    $A = $ _____

17. $b = 25.3$ cm
    $h = 12$ cm
    $A = $ _____

18. $b = 32$ cm
    $h = 16$ cm
    $A = $ _____

Solve.

19. Brian is making a kite. He needs to cut right triangles out of fabric. What is the area of a right triangle with a base of 45 cm and a height of 30 cm? _____

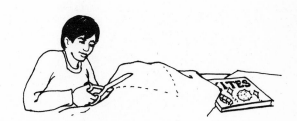

Name

Solve.

1. A swimming pool measures 40 ft by 20 ft. What is the perimeter of the pool? _____

2. Stacy practices gymnastics on a rectangular mat that is 15 ft by 20 ft. What is the area of the mat? _____

3. Carl is putting wallpaper on one wall of his kitchen. The wall measures 15 ft by 8 ft. How much wallpaper does he need? _____

4. The Lins are planning to put fencing around a rectangular garden that is 18 ft long and 12 ft wide. How much fencing do they need? _____

5. In the Lin's garden, there is a rectangular flower bed that is 6 ft long and 3 ft wide. How many square feet does the flower garden cover? _____

6. Marge is drawing a picture that measures 9 in. by 6 in. She plans to use yarn as a decorative border around the picture. How much yarn does she need? _____

7. Keith wants to tile his kitchen floor. The kitchen is a rectangle that is 14 ft by 16 ft. How many square feet of tile does he need? _____

8. The Hogans want to put carpeting in their rectangular living room, which is 15 ft by 12 ft. How many square feet of carpeting do they need? _____

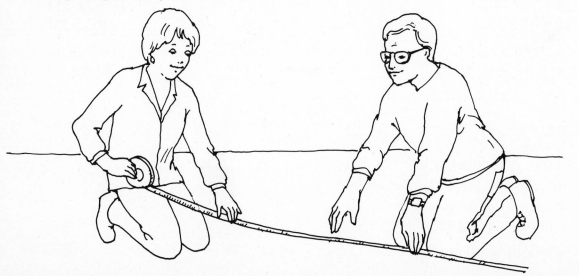

Practice

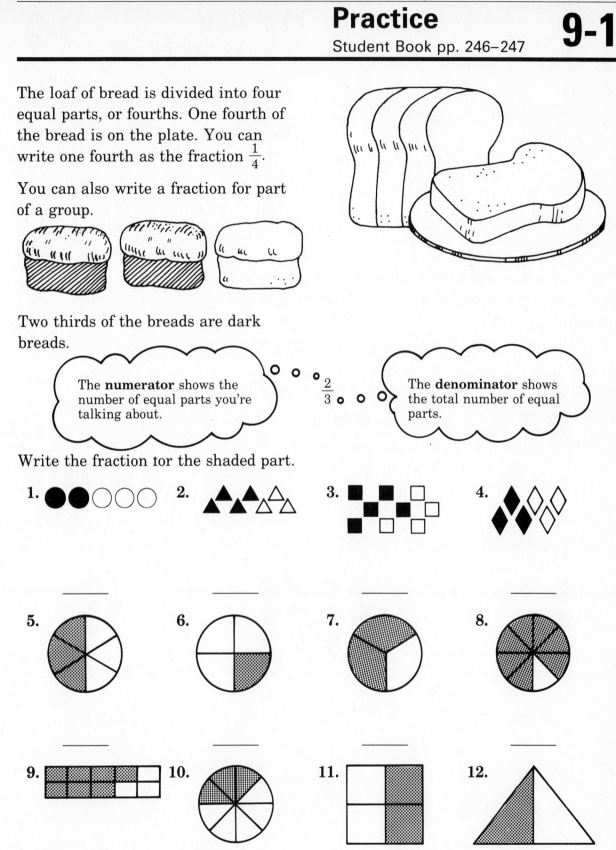

The loaf of bread is divided into four equal parts, or fourths. One fourth of the bread is on the plate. You can write one fourth as the fraction $\frac{1}{4}$.

You can also write a fraction for part of a group.

Two thirds of the breads are dark breads.

The **numerator** shows the number of equal parts you're talking about.

$\frac{2}{3}$

The **denominator** shows the total number of equal parts.

Write the fraction for the shaded part.

1. ●●○○○   2. ▲▲▲△△   3. ■■□ ■□ ■□   4. ◆◆◇◇

_____   _____   _____   _____

5.   6.   7.   8.

_____   _____   _____   _____

9.   10.   11.   12.

_____   _____   _____   _____

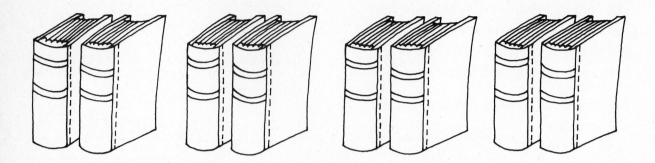

Carl borrowed 8 books from the school library. He was able to use $\frac{3}{4}$ of them when he wrote his history report. How many books did he use?

$\frac{3}{4}$ of 8 = 6   Carl was able to use 6 books for his history report.

Complete to show the number of shapes that are shaded.

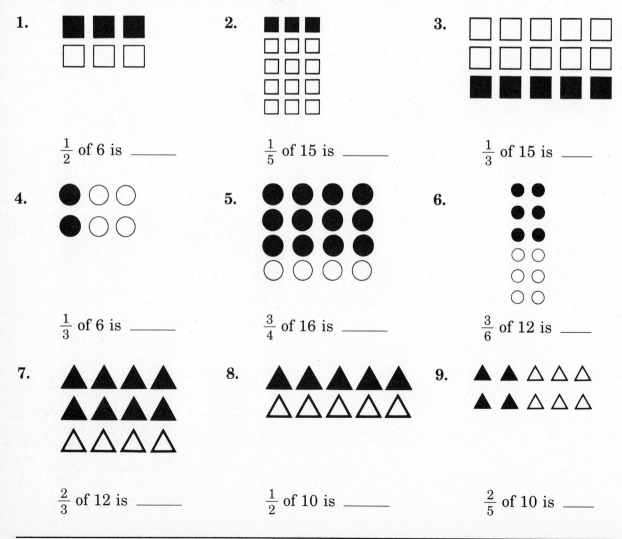

1. $\frac{1}{2}$ of 6 is _____

2. $\frac{1}{5}$ of 15 is _____

3. $\frac{1}{3}$ of 15 is _____

4. $\frac{1}{3}$ of 6 is _____

5. $\frac{3}{4}$ of 16 is _____

6. $\frac{3}{6}$ of 12 is _____

7. $\frac{2}{3}$ of 12 is _____

8. $\frac{1}{2}$ of 10 is _____

9. $\frac{2}{5}$ of 10 is _____

Practice

Student Book pp. 250–251

9-3

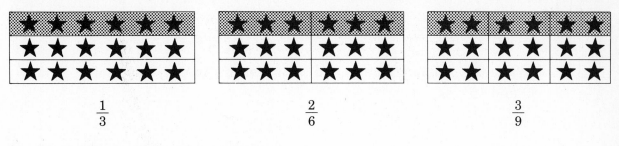

$$\frac{1}{3} \qquad \frac{2}{6} \qquad \frac{3}{9}$$

$\frac{1}{3}$, $\frac{2}{6}$, and $\frac{3}{9}$ are **equivalent fractions.**

> One way to write an equivalent fraction is to multiply the numerator and the denominator by the same number.

$$\frac{1}{3} = \frac{1 \times 2}{3 \times 2} = \frac{2}{6}$$

$$\frac{1}{3} = \frac{1 \times 3}{3 \times 3} = \frac{3}{9}$$

Complete to show an equivalent fraction.

1. $\frac{3}{4} = \frac{}{8}$

2. $\frac{3}{5} = \frac{}{10}$

3. $\frac{2}{3} = \frac{}{12}$

4. $\frac{3}{10} = \frac{}{20}$

5. $\frac{1}{2} = \frac{}{10}$

6. $\frac{1}{3} = \frac{}{9}$

7. $\frac{1}{4} = \frac{}{16}$

8. $\frac{1}{8} = \frac{}{24}$

9. $\frac{4}{5} = \frac{8}{}$

10. $\frac{1}{7} = \frac{3}{}$

11. $\frac{2}{5} = \frac{8}{}$

12. $\frac{3}{8} = \frac{6}{}$

13. $\frac{1}{6} = \frac{6}{}$

14. $\frac{1}{8} = \frac{2}{}$

15. $\frac{5}{6} = \frac{10}{}$

16. $\frac{6}{7} = \frac{18}{}$

17. $\frac{1}{6} = \frac{}{12} = \frac{}{18} = \frac{}{24}$

18. $\frac{2}{5} = \frac{}{10} = \frac{}{15} = \frac{}{20}$

19. $\frac{1}{3} = \frac{}{6} = \frac{}{9} = \frac{}{12}$

20. $\frac{4}{5} = \frac{8}{} = \frac{12}{} = \frac{16}{}$

21. $\frac{3}{4} = \frac{6}{} = \frac{9}{} = \frac{12}{}$

22. $\frac{5}{7} = \frac{10}{} = \frac{15}{} = \frac{20}{}$

Use the picture to solve.

23. Miguel colored $\frac{1}{2}$ the stars red, $\frac{1}{4}$ of the stars blue, $\frac{3}{20}$ of the stars yellow, and $\frac{1}{10}$ of the stars green. How many of each color star are there?

_____

_____

Practice
Student Book pp. 252–253

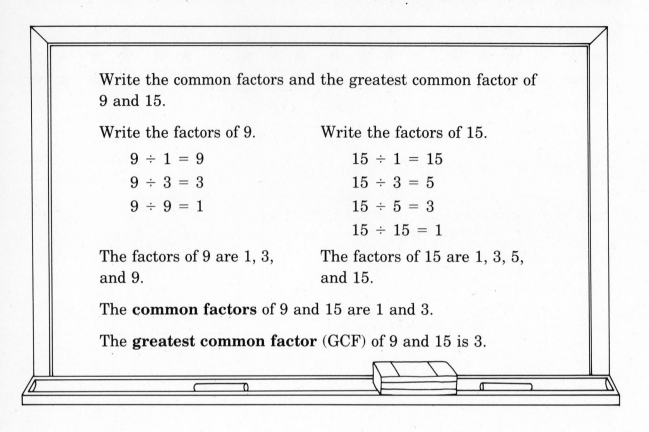

Write the common factors and the greatest common factor of 9 and 15.

Write the factors of 9.

$9 \div 1 = 9$
$9 \div 3 = 3$
$9 \div 9 = 1$

Write the factors of 15.

$15 \div 1 = 15$
$15 \div 3 = 5$
$15 \div 5 = 3$
$15 \div 15 = 1$

The factors of 9 are 1, 3, and 9.

The factors of 15 are 1, 3, 5, and 15.

The **common factors** of 9 and 15 are 1 and 3.

The **greatest common factor** (GCF) of 9 and 15 is 3.

Write the factors.

1. 16 _____
2. 12 _____
3. 10 _____
4. 5 _____
5. 21 _____
6. 14 _____
7. 18 _____
8. 24 _____

Complete the chart. Write the factors, the common factors, and the greatest common factor.

	Numbers	Factors	Common Factors	Greatest Common Factor
9.	6 and 16			
10.	12 and 15			
11.	10 and 20			
12.	15 and 24			

Practice

Student Book pp. 254–255

One way to write an equivalent fraction is to divide the terms of the fraction by the same number.

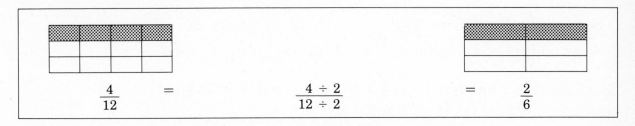

$$\frac{4}{12} \qquad = \qquad \frac{4 \div 2}{12 \div 2} \qquad = \qquad \frac{2}{6}$$

A fraction is in its **lowest terms** when you divide both terms by their greatest common factor (GCF). The GCF of 4 and 12 is 4.

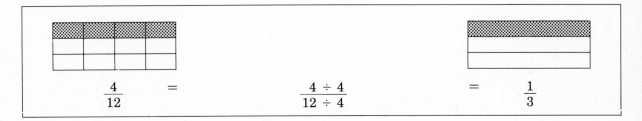

$$\frac{4}{12} \qquad = \qquad \frac{4 \div 4}{12 \div 4} \qquad = \qquad \frac{1}{3}$$

Write in lowest terms.

1. $\frac{3}{12}$ = ____ 2. $\frac{6}{8}$ = ____ 3. $\frac{5}{10}$ = ____ 4. $\frac{8}{12}$ = ____

5. $\frac{2}{6}$ = ____ 6. $\frac{8}{16}$ = ____ 7. $\frac{4}{12}$ = ____ 8. $\frac{2}{9}$ = ____

9. $\frac{3}{3}$ = ____ 10. $\frac{2}{12}$ = ____ 11. $\frac{3}{15}$ = ____ 12. $\frac{10}{20}$ = ____

13. $\frac{6}{18}$ = ____ 14. $\frac{2}{5}$ = ____ 15. $\frac{7}{21}$ = ____ 16. $\frac{20}{30}$ = ____

17. $\frac{2}{8}$ = ____ 18. $\frac{14}{21}$ = ____ 19. $\frac{15}{25}$ = ____ 20. $\frac{9}{27}$ = ____

Solve. Write your answer in lowest terms.

21. There are 64 students in the sixth grade. If 40 of the students attended the school concert, what fraction of the sixth grade went to the concert? _____

22. There are 45 students in the chorus. If 27 of them sang at the concert, what fraction of the chorus performed? _____

Name

Practice
Student Book pp. 256–257

9-6

When you multiply a whole number by 0, 1, 2, 3, and so on, the products are called **multiples** of the whole number.

| Some multiples of 2 are: 0, 2, 4, 6, 8, 10, 12, 14, 16, 18, 20. |
| Some multiples of 3 are: 0, 3, 6, 9, 12, 15, 18, 21, 24, 27, 30. |

Some common multiples of 2 and 3 are: 6, 12, and 18. The **least common multiple** (LCM) of 2 and 3 is 6.

Complete.

1. $4 \times 0 =$ _____ $4 \times 1 =$ _____ $4 \times 2 =$ _____ $4 \times 3 =$ _____ $4 \times 4 =$ _____
The first five multiples of 4 are _____, _____, _____, _____, and _____.

2. $8 \times 0 =$ _____ $8 \times 1 =$ _____ $8 \times 2 =$ _____ $8 \times 3 =$ _____ $8 \times 4 =$ _____
The first five multiples of 8 are _____, _____, _____, _____, and _____.

3. The first six multiples of 3 are _____, _____, _____, _____, _____, and _____.
The first six multiples of 5 are _____, _____, _____, _____, _____, and _____.
The LCM of 3 and 5 is _____.

Write the first two common multiples.

4. 2 and 5 _____   **5.** 3 and 6 _____   **6.** 2 and 8 _____
7. 3 and 4 _____   **8.** 3 and 5 _____   **9.** 2 and 4 _____

Write the least common multiple.

10. 4 and 9 _____   **11.** 20 and 60 _____
12. 2 and 7 _____   **13.** 5 and 8 _____
14. 3 and 4 _____   **15.** 4 and 5 _____
16. 12 and 24 _____   **17.** 6 and 8 _____
18. 25 and 50 _____   **19.** 20 and 30 _____

Solve.

20. Nan wants to buy 24 assorted stickers of rainbows, hearts, and bears. The rainbows are in packages of 3, the hearts are in packages of 6, and the bears are in packages of 4. How many of each kind of package must she buy?

_____

_____

Practice

Student Book pp. 258–259

9-7

To compare fractions with different denominators, first write equivalent fractions with like denominators. Then compare the numerators.

Compare $\frac{1}{3}$ and $\frac{3}{4}$.

$\frac{1}{3} = \frac{4}{12}$ $\qquad$ $\frac{3}{4} = \frac{9}{12}$ $\qquad\qquad$ $\frac{4}{12} < \frac{9}{12}$ $\qquad$ so $\qquad$ $\frac{1}{3} < \frac{3}{4}$

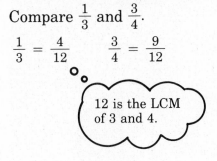

12 is the LCM of 3 and 4.

Write $<$, $>$, or $=$ to compare the fractions.

1. $\frac{2}{6}$ _____ $\frac{5}{6}$ 2. $\frac{4}{8}$ _____ $\frac{6}{8}$ 3. $\frac{2}{5}$ _____ $\frac{1}{5}$ 4. $\frac{2}{3}$ _____ $\frac{1}{3}$

5. $\frac{2}{3}$ _____ $\frac{7}{12}$ 6. $\frac{2}{5}$ _____ $\frac{3}{10}$ 7. $\frac{2}{3}$ _____ $\frac{6}{9}$ 8. $\frac{1}{2}$ _____ $\frac{5}{9}$

9. $\frac{1}{2}$ _____ $\frac{2}{5}$ 10. $\frac{2}{3}$ _____ $\frac{1}{4}$ 11. $\frac{3}{12}$ _____ $\frac{2}{4}$ 12. $\frac{3}{9}$ _____ $\frac{1}{2}$

13. $\frac{1}{2}$ _____ $\frac{2}{7}$ 14. $\frac{3}{4}$ _____ $\frac{5}{6}$ 15. $\frac{5}{7}$ _____ $\frac{10}{14}$ 16. $\frac{1}{3}$ _____ $\frac{1}{5}$

Use the LCD to write the fractions in order from the least to the greatest.

17. $\frac{2}{9}, \frac{1}{2}, \frac{1}{3}, \frac{1}{6}$ 18. $\frac{2}{5}, \frac{1}{2}, \frac{3}{10}, \frac{3}{5}$ 19. $\frac{2}{6}, \frac{1}{2}, \frac{1}{9}, \frac{2}{9}$

_____ _____ _____

20. $\frac{2}{3}, \frac{3}{4}, \frac{2}{8}, \frac{1}{2}$ 21. $\frac{5}{6}, \frac{3}{8}, \frac{1}{2}, \frac{3}{4}$ 22. $\frac{2}{3}, \frac{2}{9}, \frac{1}{2}, \frac{5}{6}$

_____ _____ _____

Write the greater measurement.

23. $\frac{3}{4}$ in. or $\frac{7}{8}$ in. _____ 24. $\frac{1}{3}$ yd or $\frac{3}{8}$ yd _____

Practice
Student Book pp. 260–261

Study the patterns in these drawings. Write the letter of the one that is different.

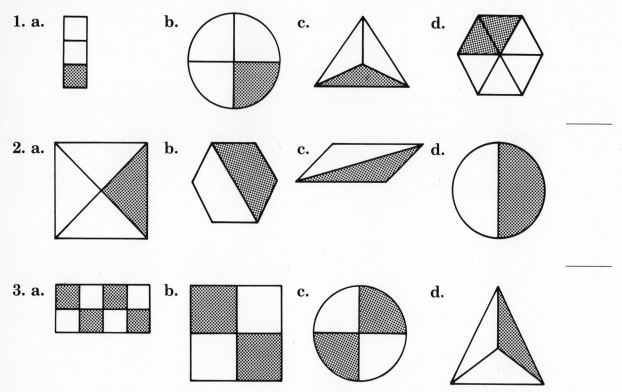

1. a.   b.   c.   d. _____

2. a.   b.   c.   d. _____

3. a.   b.   c.   d. _____

Write the next three fractions in the pattern.

4. $\frac{1}{3}, \frac{1}{5}, \frac{1}{7}, \frac{1}{9}, \frac{1}{11},$ _____

5. $\frac{1}{32}, \frac{1}{28}, \frac{1}{24}, \frac{1}{20}, \frac{1}{16},$ _____

6. $\frac{1}{2}, \frac{2}{4}, \frac{4}{8}, \frac{8}{16},$ _____

7. $\frac{2}{3}, \frac{4}{6}, \frac{6}{9}, \frac{8}{12}, \frac{10}{15},$ _____

8. $\frac{51}{100}, \frac{45}{100}, \frac{39}{100}, \frac{33}{100},$ _____

9. $\frac{3}{4}, \frac{5}{6}, \frac{7}{8}, \frac{9}{10}, \frac{11}{12},$ _____

10. $\frac{11}{99}, \frac{12}{108}, \frac{13}{117}, \frac{14}{126}$ _____

11. $\frac{3}{45}, \frac{5}{75}, \frac{7}{105}, \frac{9}{135},$ _____

Practice

9-9

Fractions can be greater than 1.

Darlene cut each of her oranges into 4 pieces. She ate $\frac{9}{4}$ oranges.
We can write $\frac{9}{4}$ as a **mixed number.**

| Divide the numerator by the denominator. | Then write any remainder over the divisor. |

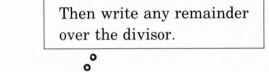

Write as a whole number or a mixed number in lowest terms.

1. $\frac{15}{5} =$ _____

2. $\frac{5}{2} =$ _____

3. $\frac{16}{4} =$ _____

4. $\frac{21}{3} =$ _____

5. $\frac{8}{3} =$ _____

6. $\frac{20}{4} =$ _____

7. $\frac{16}{5} =$ _____

8. $\frac{7}{2} =$ _____

9. $\frac{32}{10} =$ _____

10. $\frac{14}{4} =$ _____

11. $\frac{20}{8} =$ _____

12. $\frac{43}{8} =$ _____

Solve. Write the answer as a whole number or a mixed number in lowest terms.

13. Joe cut oranges in half. He had 15 halves on the table. How many oranges were there? _____

14. Margo cut apples in fourths. She had 24 pieces of apple on the table. How many apples were there?

_____

15. Together Joe and Margo had 75 bananas. If they divided them equally, how many would each child get? _____

Name

A recipe for making whole wheat
bread calls for $3\frac{1}{2}$ c of flour.
You can write $3\frac{1}{2}$ as a fraction.

Multiply the whole number by the denominator.	Add the numerator to the product.	Write the sum over the denominator.
$3 \times 2 = 6$	$6 + 1 = 7$	$\frac{7}{2}$

Write as a fraction.

1. $2\frac{3}{4} =$ _____ 2. $6\frac{2}{5} =$ _____ 3. $5\frac{9}{10} =$ _____ 4. $4\frac{1}{6} =$ _____

5. $8\frac{2}{3} =$ _____ 6. $7\frac{3}{8} =$ _____ 7. $3\frac{2}{7} =$ _____ 8. $3\frac{3}{11} =$ _____

9. $4\frac{3}{5} =$ _____ 10. $8\frac{6}{7} =$ _____ 11. $5\frac{2}{9} =$ _____ 12. $1\frac{7}{10} =$ _____

13. $2\frac{5}{8} =$ _____ 14. $6\frac{4}{5} =$ _____ 15. $4\frac{1}{9} =$ _____ 16. $5\frac{2}{11} =$ _____

17. $3\frac{5}{12} =$ _____ 18. $7\frac{5}{6} =$ _____ 19. $5\frac{3}{7} =$ _____ 20. $4\frac{5}{8} =$ _____

Solve.

21. Tom needs $2\frac{2}{3}$ c rye flour to make bread. He has $\frac{7}{2}$ c of flour. Does he have enough flour to make the bread? _____

22. Kim's recipe called for $1\frac{3}{4}$ c of milk. She has $\frac{5}{3}$ c. Does she have enough milk to make the recipe? _____

This ruler shows *inches* and parts of an inch.

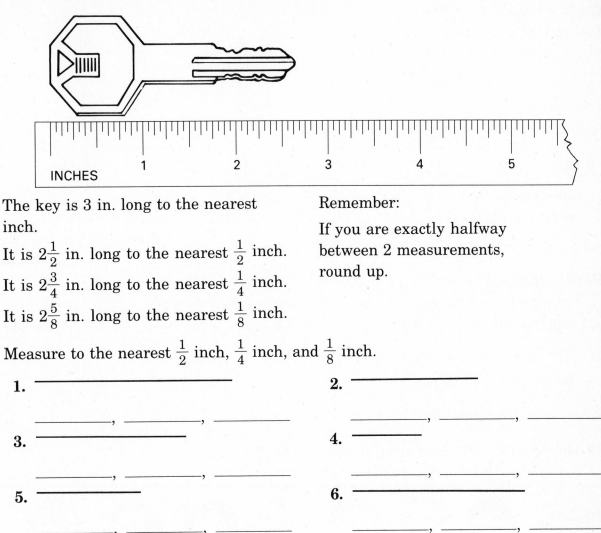

The key is 3 in. long to the nearest inch.

It is $2\frac{1}{2}$ in. long to the nearest $\frac{1}{2}$ inch.

It is $2\frac{3}{4}$ in. long to the nearest $\frac{1}{4}$ inch.

It is $2\frac{5}{8}$ in. long to the nearest $\frac{1}{8}$ inch.

Remember:

If you are exactly halfway between 2 measurements, round up.

Measure to the nearest $\frac{1}{2}$ inch, $\frac{1}{4}$ inch, and $\frac{1}{8}$ inch.

1. _____

_____ , _____ , _____

2. _____

_____ , _____ , _____

3. _____

_____ , _____ , _____

4. _____

_____ , _____ , _____

5. _____

_____ , _____ , _____

6. _____

_____ , _____ , _____

Draw segments of the given length. Then write >, <, or = to complete.

7. $2\frac{1}{4}$ in. ☐ $2\frac{1}{2}$ in.

8. $\frac{3}{4}$ in. ☐ $\frac{5}{8}$ in.

9. $3\frac{1}{4}$ in. ☐ $3\frac{5}{8}$ in.

10. $2\frac{1}{2}$ in. ☐ $2\frac{3}{4}$ in.

11. $1\frac{1}{2}$ in. ☐ $1\frac{2}{4}$ in.

Practice

Is the fraction less than, equal to, or greater than one half?
Write $<$, $>$, or $=$.

1. $\frac{3}{6}$ _____

2. $\frac{5}{8}$ _____

3. $\frac{3}{10}$ _____

4. $\frac{9}{16}$ _____

5. $\frac{5}{12}$ _____

6. $\frac{7}{14}$ _____

7. $\frac{12}{20}$ _____

8. $\frac{6}{18}$ _____

Round to the nearest whole number.

9. $3\frac{1}{2}$ _____

10. $4\frac{1}{4}$ _____

11. $8\frac{5}{8}$ _____

12. $13\frac{1}{3}$ _____

13. $7\frac{1}{6}$ _____

14. $9\frac{2}{3}$ _____

15. $11\frac{3}{4}$ _____

16. $10\frac{5}{6}$ _____

Solve by rounding to the nearest whole number.

17. Jack played soccer for $2\frac{1}{3}$ h on Friday, $1\frac{3}{4}$ h on Saturday, and $2\frac{1}{2}$ h on Sunday. For about how many hours did Jack play soccer? _____

18. Three brothers are $4\frac{1}{2}$ ft, $5\frac{7}{8}$ ft, and $3\frac{3}{8}$ ft tall. About how tall is each boy? _____

Solve by rounding the fraction to $\frac{1}{2}$ or to 1.

19. Brian said that $\frac{7}{12}$ of the 24 boys in the scout troop went camping. About how many boys went camping? _____

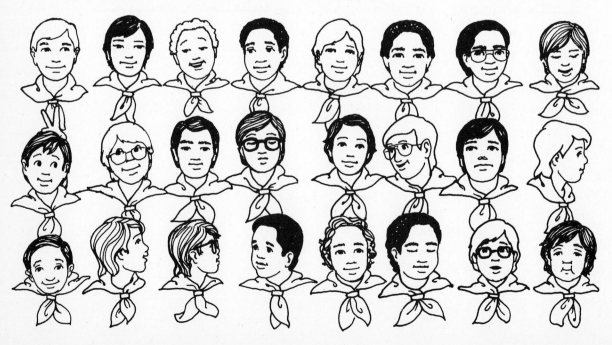

Name

Use the diagrams to complete the sentence. Write *all*,
some or *no*.

odd numbers   even numbers

1. _____ odd numbers are even numbers.

2. _____ even numbers are odd numbers.

3. _____ odd numbers are not even numbers.

whole numbers (odd numbers)

4. _____ odd numbers are whole numbers.

5. _____ whole numbers are odd numbers.

6. _____ whole numbers are not odd numbers.

fractions (fractions with 2 as a denominator)

7. _____ fractions with 2 as a denominator are fractions.

8. _____ fractions are fractions with 2 as a denominator.

9. _____ fractions are not fractions with 2 as a denominator.

baseball players (catchers)

10. _____ catchers are baseball players.

11. _____ baseball players are catchers.

12. _____ baseball players are not catchers.

squares   circles

13. _____ squares are not circles.

14. _____ circles are squares.

15. _____ squares are circles.

polygons (squares)

16. _____ polygons are not squares.

17. _____ squares are polygons.

18. _____ polygons are squares.

Charles has a truck collection. Four ninths of the trucks have wheels missing. Two ninths of the trucks need painting. What part of the collection needs repair?

To find the answer, add $\frac{4}{9}$ and $\frac{2}{9}$.

Since the denominators are the same, you add the numerator and keep the same denominator. Write the answer in lowest terms.

$$\frac{4}{9} + \frac{2}{9} = \frac{6}{9} = \frac{2}{3}$$

Two thirds of the collection needs repair.

Add or subtract. Write the answer in lowest terms.

1. $\frac{1}{5} + \frac{3}{5} =$ _____   2. $\frac{2}{6} + \frac{1}{6} =$ _____   3. $\frac{4}{9} + \frac{2}{9} =$ _____   4. $\frac{5}{8} - \frac{3}{8} =$ _____

5. $\frac{3}{14} + \frac{4}{14} =$ _____   6. $\frac{2}{6} + \frac{4}{6} =$ _____   7. $\frac{1}{8} + \frac{1}{8} =$ _____   8. $\frac{5}{6} - \frac{2}{6} =$ _____

9. $\begin{array}{r} \frac{5}{9} \\ -\frac{2}{9} \\ \hline \end{array}$ 10. $\begin{array}{r} \frac{6}{8} \\ +\frac{3}{8} \\ \hline \end{array}$ 11. $\begin{array}{r} \frac{9}{10} \\ -\frac{7}{10} \\ \hline \end{array}$ 12. $\begin{array}{r} \frac{2}{5} \\ +\frac{3}{5} \\ \hline \end{array}$ 13. $\begin{array}{r} \frac{5}{12} \\ +\frac{1}{12} \\ \hline \end{array}$

14. $\begin{array}{r} \frac{2}{3} \\ +\frac{2}{3} \\ \hline \end{array}$ 15. $\begin{array}{r} \frac{20}{9} \\ -\frac{2}{9} \\ \hline \end{array}$ 16. $\begin{array}{r} \frac{3}{8} \\ +\frac{3}{8} \\ \hline \end{array}$ 17. $\begin{array}{r} \frac{14}{7} \\ +\frac{4}{7} \\ \hline \end{array}$ 18. $\begin{array}{r} \frac{15}{16} \\ -\frac{11}{16} \\ \hline \end{array}$

Solve. Write the answer in lowest terms.

19. One truck has 6 tires. Half of the tires are flat. How many tires are flat? _____

20. Seven twelfths of the trucks in Charles's collection are to be painted red. Charles has painted five twelfths of them. What fraction of the trucks does he have left to paint red? _____

To add fractions with different denominators, follow the steps below.

Rename using the least common denominator (LCD) of the fractions.

Now, add the fractions.

The LCD of $\frac{1}{2}$ and $\frac{1}{4}$ is 4.

$$\frac{1}{2} = \frac{2}{4}$$
$$+\frac{1}{4} = \frac{1}{4}$$

$$\frac{1}{2} = \frac{2}{4}$$
$$+\frac{1}{4} = +\frac{1}{4}$$
$$\frac{3}{4}$$

Write the sum in lowest terms.

1. $\frac{1}{3}$ $+\frac{1}{6}$

2. $\frac{1}{9}$ $+\frac{1}{3}$

3. $\frac{1}{4}$ $+\frac{3}{8}$

4. $\frac{1}{10}$ $+\frac{2}{5}$

5. $\frac{2}{3}$ $+\frac{1}{9}$

6. $\frac{2}{12}$ $+\frac{2}{4}$

7. $\frac{6}{14}$ $+\frac{3}{7}$

8. $\frac{1}{2}$ $+\frac{3}{8}$

9. $\frac{6}{7}$ $+\frac{3}{14}$

10. $\frac{4}{5}$ $+\frac{4}{15}$

11. $\frac{5}{18}$ $+\frac{2}{9}$

12. $\frac{3}{5}$ $+\frac{7}{20}$

13. $\frac{7}{12}$ $+\frac{2}{3}$

14. $\frac{4}{6}$ $+\frac{3}{18}$

15. $\frac{7}{6}$ $+\frac{5}{12}$

16. $\frac{2}{9} + \frac{2}{3} =$ _____

17. $\frac{2}{5} + \frac{7}{10} =$ _____

18. $\frac{1}{2} + \frac{7}{8} =$ _____

19. $\frac{5}{8} + \frac{3}{4} =$ _____

20. $\frac{3}{10} + \frac{9}{20} =$ _____

21. $\frac{2}{3} + \frac{4}{9} =$ _____

Solve. Write the answer in lowest terms.

22. Julio spends $\frac{5}{12}$ h making favors for a graduation party. Ruth spends $\frac{2}{3}$ h. How much time do they spend in all making favors? _____

23. They needed $\frac{7}{9}$ yd of ribbon for the favors and $\frac{2}{3}$ yd of ribbon for the tables. How much ribbon did they need in all? _____

Name _____

Add. Write the sum in lowest terms.

1. $\dfrac{1}{4}$
$+\dfrac{5}{6}$
_____

2. $\dfrac{1}{2}$
$+\dfrac{1}{3}$
_____

3. $\dfrac{1}{3}$
$+\dfrac{3}{5}$
_____

4. $\dfrac{5}{12}$
$+\dfrac{1}{2}$
_____

5. $\dfrac{3}{5}$
$+\dfrac{1}{2}$
_____

6. $\dfrac{9}{10}$
$+\dfrac{3}{4}$
_____

7. $\dfrac{3}{4}$
$+\dfrac{1}{2}$
_____

8. $\dfrac{1}{4}$
$+\dfrac{4}{5}$
_____

9. $\dfrac{5}{6}$
$+\dfrac{1}{2}$
_____

10. $\dfrac{11}{15}$
$+\dfrac{2}{3}$
_____

11. $\dfrac{2}{3}$
$+\dfrac{5}{6}$
_____

12. $\dfrac{1}{2}$
$+\dfrac{7}{8}$
_____

13. $\dfrac{7}{12}$
$+\dfrac{3}{4}$
_____

14. $\dfrac{1}{2}$
$+\dfrac{7}{10}$
_____

15. $\dfrac{1}{5}$
$+\dfrac{5}{6}$
_____

16. $\dfrac{2}{3}$
$+\dfrac{3}{4}$
_____

17. $\dfrac{7}{8} + \dfrac{3}{4} =$ _____

18. $\dfrac{1}{6} + \dfrac{11}{12} =$ _____

19. $\dfrac{9}{10} + \dfrac{4}{5} =$ _____

Solve.

20. It took Marla $\frac{2}{3}$ h to vacuum the house and $\frac{1}{4}$ h to dust the living room. How long did it take her to do the two tasks? _____

21. Richard washed the bathroom and kitchen floors, which took $\frac{2}{5}$ h. Then he washed several windows, which took $\frac{5}{6}$ h. How long did Richard spend at the two tasks? _____

Practice
Student Book pp. 286–287 **10-4**

Charlotte made the costumes for the school play. When she made her queen's costume, she used $2\frac{1}{8}$ yd of purple material and $1\frac{1}{4}$ yd of gold material. How much material did she use altogether?

To solve, add $2\frac{1}{8}$ and $1\frac{1}{4}$.

Write equivalent fractions with the LCD.

$$2\frac{1}{8} = 2\frac{1}{8}$$
$$+1\frac{1}{4} = +1\frac{2}{8}$$

Add the fractions.

$$\begin{array}{r} 2\frac{1}{8} \\ +1\frac{2}{8} \\ \hline \frac{3}{8} \end{array}$$

Add the whole numbers.

$$\begin{array}{r} 2\frac{1}{8} \\ +1\frac{2}{8} \\ \hline 3\frac{3}{8} \end{array}$$

Charlotte used $3\frac{3}{8}$ yd of material.

Add. Write the sum in lowest terms.

1. $\begin{array}{r} 2\frac{1}{4} \\ +1\frac{1}{8} \\ \hline \end{array}$

2. $\begin{array}{r} 6\frac{1}{3} \\ +1\frac{1}{5} \\ \hline \end{array}$

3. $\begin{array}{r} 4\frac{1}{9} \\ +2\frac{1}{3} \\ \hline \end{array}$

4. $\begin{array}{r} 5\frac{1}{4} \\ +3\frac{1}{3} \\ \hline \end{array}$

5. $\begin{array}{r} 4\frac{2}{5} \\ +4\frac{2}{10} \\ \hline \end{array}$

6. $\begin{array}{r} 7\frac{1}{4} \\ +3\frac{2}{5} \\ \hline \end{array}$

7. $\begin{array}{r} 9\frac{1}{6} \\ +\frac{2}{3} \\ \hline \end{array}$

8. $\begin{array}{r} 1\frac{1}{8} \\ +3\frac{2}{5} \\ \hline \end{array}$

9. $\begin{array}{r} 1\frac{3}{8} \\ +2\frac{1}{6} \\ \hline \end{array}$

10. $\begin{array}{r} 1 \\ +3\frac{5}{6} \\ \hline \end{array}$

11. $\begin{array}{r} \frac{1}{7} \\ +3\frac{3}{28} \\ \hline \end{array}$

12. $\begin{array}{r} 6\frac{1}{4} \\ +3\frac{1}{6} \\ \hline \end{array}$

13. $5\frac{1}{6} + 2\frac{2}{3} =$ _____

14. $4\frac{1}{8} + 2\frac{2}{3} =$ _____

15. $2\frac{4}{7} + 1\frac{1}{14} =$ _____

Solve.

16. Charlotte worked on the costumes for $3\frac{1}{6}$ h on Saturday and $2\frac{1}{4}$ h on Sunday. How many hours did she work on the two days? _____

Practice

Student Book pp. 288–289

When you add mixed numbers, sometimes you need to rename the sum.

Add $1\frac{5}{8}$ and $1\frac{3}{4}$.

Write equivalent fractions with the LCD.

$$1\frac{5}{8} = 1\frac{5}{8}$$
$$+1\frac{3}{4} = +1\frac{6}{8}$$

Add the fractions. Then add the whole numbers.

$$1\frac{5}{8}$$
$$+1\frac{6}{8}$$
$$\overline{2\frac{11}{8}}$$

Rename the sum.

$$1\frac{5}{8}$$
$$+1\frac{6}{8}$$
$$\overline{2\frac{11}{8}} = 2 + 1\frac{3}{8} = 3\frac{3}{8}$$

Add. Write the sum in lowest terms.

1. $3\frac{3}{6}$
   $+1\frac{2}{3}$

2. $2\frac{5}{8}$
   $+2\frac{3}{4}$

3. $3\frac{7}{10}$
   $+4\frac{4}{5}$

4. $5\frac{1}{3}$
   $+4\frac{3}{4}$

5. $6\frac{2}{3}$
   $+2\frac{3}{5}$

6. $7\frac{2}{3}$
   $+1\frac{4}{8}$

7. $3\frac{7}{9}$
   $+\frac{2}{9}$

8. $4\frac{3}{5}$
   $+1\frac{2}{6}$

9. $3\frac{3}{8} + 2\frac{2}{5} = $ _____

10. $7\frac{9}{10} + 2\frac{3}{4} = $ _____

Solve. Write the answer in lowest terms.

11. Sue filled $2\frac{1}{2}$ cartons with records. She filled another $3\frac{3}{4}$ cartons with books. How many cartons did she fill? _____

12. Bob filled $5\frac{3}{4}$ cartons with baseball cards. He filled $3\frac{2}{3}$ more cartons with football cards. How many cartons did he fill? _____

13. Margo had $6\frac{1}{4}$ cartons filled with books. She filled another $2\frac{1}{2}$ cartons. How many cartons were filled altogether? _____

Practice
Student Book pp. 290–291

Sometimes you aren't given all the information you need to solve a problem. Sometimes you are given more information than you need.

Too Much Information	**Too Little Information**
Gladstone Zoo was founded in 1858. Fairmont Zoo was started a century later. Yellowstone Zoo was founded in 1896. When was Fairmont Zoo founded?	On Saturday and Sunday, 1436 people visited Gladstone Zoo. On Sunday, $\frac{1}{2}$ of the people who came made a donation of $1.00. How much money was donated?
<u>Fact not needed:</u> Yellowstone Zoo was founded in 1896.	<u>Missing fact:</u> The number of people who came on Sunday.
<u>Facts needed:</u> Gladstone Zoo was founded in 1858. Fairmont Zoo was founded 100 years later. $1858 + 100 = 1958$ Fairmont Zoo was founded in 1958.	You cannot solve this problem without more information.

Read each problem. Write *TM* if there is too much information and *TL* if there is too little. Solve the problems with too much information.

1. Gladstone Zoo added 8 lions to their collection. They now have $\frac{1}{2}$ doz more lions than Fairmont Zoo. How many lions do they have?

    _____

2. Fairmont Zoo has a rattlesnake that measures $6\frac{1}{2}$ ft in length. The rattlesnake at Gladstone Zoo is 65 in. long and weighs 12 lb. How much longer is Fairmont's snake?

    _____

3. Fairmont Zoo is open 8 h each day except Monday, when it is closed. Gladstone Zoo is open the same number of hours. How many hours a week is Fairmont Zoo open?

    _____

4. There is a 1-hour difference in daily opening times between the two zoos. Fairmont Zoo opens at 10 A.M. When does Gladstone Zoo open?

    _____

Practice

Student Book pp. 292–293 **10-7**

To subtract fractions with different denominators, follow the steps below.

First, rewrite the fractions using the least common denominator (LCD).

The LCD of $\frac{1}{2}$ and $\frac{1}{4}$ is 4.

$\frac{1}{2} = \frac{2}{4}$
$-\frac{1}{4} = \frac{1}{4}$

Then, subtract the fractions.

$\begin{array}{r} \frac{2}{4} \\ -\frac{1}{4} \\ \hline \frac{1}{4} \end{array}$

Subtract. Write the difference in lowest terms.

1. $\begin{array}{r} \frac{3}{4} \\ -\frac{1}{12} \\ \hline \end{array}$

2. $\begin{array}{r} \frac{5}{8} \\ -\frac{1}{2} \\ \hline \end{array}$

3. $\begin{array}{r} \frac{6}{9} \\ -\frac{1}{3} \\ \hline \end{array}$

4. $\begin{array}{r} \frac{4}{5} \\ -\frac{1}{10} \\ \hline \end{array}$

5. $\begin{array}{r} \frac{3}{4} \\ -\frac{1}{8} \\ \hline \end{array}$

6. $\begin{array}{r} \frac{2}{3} \\ -\frac{1}{6} \\ \hline \end{array}$

7. $\begin{array}{r} \frac{5}{4} \\ -\frac{3}{8} \\ \hline \end{array}$

8. $\begin{array}{r} \frac{9}{10} \\ -\frac{2}{5} \\ \hline \end{array}$

9. $\begin{array}{r} \frac{13}{25} \\ -\frac{1}{5} \\ \hline \end{array}$

10. $\begin{array}{r} \frac{11}{12} \\ -\frac{3}{4} \\ \hline \end{array}$

11. $\begin{array}{r} \frac{5}{8} \\ -\frac{1}{4} \\ \hline \end{array}$

12. $\begin{array}{r} \frac{4}{9} \\ -\frac{1}{3} \\ \hline \end{array}$

Solve.

13. It takes Jamie $\frac{3}{4}$ h to wash his father's car. It takes his sister Marianne $\frac{5}{12}$ h. How much longer does it take Jamie? _____

Practice

Student Book pp. 294–295 **10-8**

To subtract $\frac{2}{3}$ from $\frac{3}{4}$ first rewrite the fractions using the LCD.
Then subtract.

$$
\begin{array}{r}
\frac{3}{4} = \frac{9}{12} \\
-\frac{2}{3} = -\frac{8}{12} \\
\hline
\frac{1}{12}
\end{array}
$$

The difference is $\frac{1}{12}$.

Subtract. Write the difference in lowest terms.

1. $\frac{3}{4}$
   $-\frac{1}{6}$

2. $\frac{7}{9}$
   $-\frac{1}{3}$

3. $\frac{5}{8}$
   $-\frac{1}{2}$

4. $\frac{7}{8}$
   $-\frac{1}{4}$

5. $\frac{5}{6}$
   $-\frac{1}{2}$

6. $\frac{6}{7}$
   $-\frac{2}{3}$

7. $\frac{4}{5}$
   $-\frac{1}{3}$

8. $\frac{5}{6}$
   $-\frac{3}{4}$

9. $\frac{9}{10}$
   $-\frac{1}{2}$

10. $\frac{3}{4}$
    $-\frac{5}{12}$

11. $\frac{8}{9}$
    $-\frac{1}{2}$

12. $\frac{2}{9}$
    $-\frac{1}{6}$

13. $\frac{2}{3} - \frac{1}{4} =$ _____

14. $\frac{5}{8} - \frac{1}{6} =$ _____

15. $\frac{4}{5} - \frac{1}{2} =$ _____

16. $\frac{4}{5} - \frac{1}{4} =$ _____

17. $\frac{5}{8} - \frac{1}{3} =$ _____

18. $\frac{3}{8} - \frac{1}{3} =$ _____

Solve.

19. In one year, Miguel grew $\frac{5}{8}$ in. During that same year, Albert grew $\frac{5}{16}$ in. Who grew more and by how much?

_____

A killer whale measured $23\frac{1}{2}$ ft long.
A beluga whale was $12\frac{1}{4}$ ft in length.
To find out how much longer the killer
whale was, subtract $12\frac{1}{4}$ from $23\frac{1}{2}$.

Write equivalent fractions with the LCD.	Subtract the fractions.	Subtract the whole numbers.
$23\frac{1}{2} = 23\frac{2}{4}$ $-12\frac{1}{4} = -12\frac{1}{4}$	$23\frac{2}{4}$ $-12\frac{1}{4}$ $\frac{1}{4}$	$23\frac{2}{4}$ $-12\frac{1}{4}$ $11\frac{1}{4}$

The killer whale was $11\frac{1}{4}$ ft longer than the beluga whale.

Subtract. Write the difference in lowest terms.

1. $4\frac{7}{8}$
    $-2\frac{1}{2}$

2. $3\frac{4}{7}$
    $-2\frac{1}{3}$

3. $16\frac{3}{4}$
    $-3\frac{2}{3}$

4. $9\frac{8}{10}$
    $-2\frac{2}{5}$

5. $18\frac{4}{6}$
    $-5\frac{1}{3}$

6. $12\frac{5}{6}$
    $-3\frac{2}{4}$

7. $8\frac{3}{8}$
    -4

8. $9\frac{9}{10}$
    $-7\frac{1}{2}$

9. $5\frac{3}{8}$
    $-4\frac{1}{5}$

10. $9\frac{2}{3}$
    $-6\frac{1}{4}$

11. $12\frac{8}{9}$
    $-5\frac{2}{3}$

12. $8\frac{4}{5}$
    $-\frac{1}{2}$

13. $3\frac{7}{8} - 1\frac{2}{3} = $ _____

14. $8\frac{1}{2} - 4 = $ _____

15. $12\frac{5}{6} - 11 = $ _____

16. $8\frac{3}{5} - 5\frac{1}{3} = $ _____

Solve.

17. A fishing boat that was doing research on whales was
$56\frac{3}{8}$ ft long. A second boat was 4 ft shorter. How long was
the second boat? _____

Practice

Student Book pp. 298–299

10-10

The Chans bought 60 lb of meat. In 7 weeks, they used $42\frac{1}{2}$ lb. To find out how much meat is left, subtract $42\frac{1}{2}$ from 60.

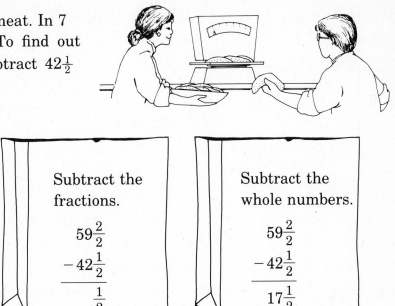

Regroup 60 as $59\frac{2}{2}$.

$$60 = 59\frac{2}{2}$$
$$-42\frac{1}{2} = -42\frac{1}{2}$$

Subtract the fractions.

$$59\frac{2}{2}$$
$$-42\frac{1}{2}$$
$$\overline{\qquad \frac{1}{2}}$$

Subtract the whole numbers.

$$59\frac{2}{2}$$
$$-42\frac{1}{2}$$
$$\overline{17\frac{1}{2}}$$

The Chans have $17\frac{1}{2}$ lb of meat left.

Subtract. Write the difference in lowest terms.

1. $\begin{array}{r} 7 \\ -2\frac{3}{5} \\ \hline \end{array}$
2. $\begin{array}{r} 6 \\ -\frac{5}{8} \\ \hline \end{array}$
3. $\begin{array}{r} 4 \\ -1\frac{1}{4} \\ \hline \end{array}$
4. $\begin{array}{r} 9 \\ -5\frac{4}{6} \\ \hline \end{array}$

5. $\begin{array}{r} 10 \\ -5\frac{1}{3} \\ \hline \end{array}$
6. $\begin{array}{r} 14 \\ -6\frac{4}{6} \\ \hline \end{array}$
7. $\begin{array}{r} 9 \\ -2\frac{2}{5} \\ \hline \end{array}$
8. $\begin{array}{r} 8 \\ -2\frac{6}{8} \\ \hline \end{array}$

9. $9 - 4\frac{2}{3} = $ _____
10. $10 - 5\frac{5}{9} = $ _____

11. $8 - 2\frac{8}{10} = $ _____
12. $3 - 2\frac{1}{8} = $ _____

13. $12 - 6\frac{3}{7} = $ _____
14. $7 - 2\frac{3}{4} = $ _____

Solve.

15. The Chans bought 24 lb of vegetables. In 7 weeks, they used $18\frac{3}{4}$ lb. How many pounds of vegetables are left?

_____

Name _____

When you subtract mixed numbers, sometimes you first need to rename.

Subtract $2\frac{3}{8}$ from $4\frac{1}{8}$.

Rename $4\frac{1}{8}$ as $3\frac{9}{8}$.

$$4\frac{1}{8} = 3\frac{9}{8}$$
$$-2\frac{3}{8} = -2\frac{3}{8}$$

Subtract the fractions.

$$3\frac{9}{8}$$
$$-2\frac{3}{8}$$
$$\overline{\frac{6}{8}}$$

Subtract the whole numbers.

$$3\frac{9}{8}$$
$$-2\frac{3}{8}$$
$$\overline{1\frac{6}{8} = 1\frac{3}{4}}$$

Subtract. Write the difference in lowest terms.

1. $6\frac{1}{3}$
   $-4\frac{2}{3}$

2. $7\frac{3}{5}$
   $-1\frac{4}{5}$

3. $9\frac{2}{8}$
   $-2\frac{5}{8}$

4. $4\frac{1}{6}$
   $-\frac{5}{6}$

5. 8
   $-3\frac{3}{9}$

6. $9\frac{1}{10}$
   $-6\frac{3}{10}$

7. $4\frac{1}{11}$
   $-2\frac{5}{11}$

8. $6\frac{3}{7}$
   $-4\frac{4}{7}$

9. $7\frac{1}{4} - 3\frac{3}{4} =$ _____

10. $9\frac{1}{6} - 5\frac{2}{6} =$ _____

11. $3\frac{2}{8} - 1\frac{3}{8} =$ _____

12. $4 - 2\frac{4}{12} =$ _____

13. $8\frac{1}{3} - 2\frac{2}{3} =$ _____

14. $10\frac{2}{5} - 5\frac{3}{5} =$ _____

Solve. Write the answer in lowest terms.

15. Mary jumped $6\frac{3}{8}$ ft. Joe jumped $5\frac{5}{8}$ ft. How much farther did Mary jump? _____

16. Steven jumped $4\frac{1}{3}$ ft. Betsy jumped $2\frac{2}{3}$ ft. How much farther did Steven jump? _____

Practice

Student Book pp. 302–303

Carlos weighs $75\frac{1}{5}$ lb. Suzanne weighs $72\frac{1}{2}$ lb. To find out how much more Carlos weighs, subtract $72\frac{1}{2}$ from $75\frac{1}{5}$.

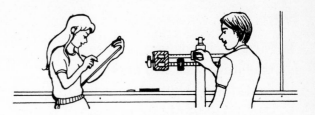

Write equivalent fractions with the LCD.

$$75\frac{1}{5} = \quad 75\frac{2}{10}$$
$$-72\frac{1}{2} = \quad -72\frac{5}{10}$$

Rename $75\frac{2}{10}$ as $74\frac{12}{10}$.

$$75\frac{2}{10} = \quad 74\frac{12}{10}$$
$$-72\frac{5}{10} = \quad -72\frac{5}{10}$$

Subtract.

$$74\frac{12}{10}$$
$$-72\frac{5}{10}$$
$$\overline{\quad 2\frac{7}{10}}$$

Carlos weighs $2\frac{7}{10}$ lb more than Suzanne.

Subtract. Write the difference in lowest terms.

1. $\quad 4\frac{2}{8}$
$\quad -1\frac{4}{5}$

2. $\quad 7\frac{2}{4}$
$\quad -3\frac{5}{6}$

3. $\quad 12\frac{1}{2}$
$\quad -\;6\frac{3}{5}$

4. $\quad 9\frac{2}{8}$
$\quad -2\frac{1}{3}$

5. $\quad 6\frac{2}{7}$
$\quad -2\frac{1}{2}$

6. $\quad 5\frac{3}{5}$
$\quad -1\frac{3}{4}$

7. $\quad 10\frac{1}{2}$
$\quad -\;5\frac{5}{8}$

8. $\quad 6$
$\quad -2\frac{2}{3}$

9. $\quad 9\frac{2}{6}$
$\quad -1\frac{2}{3}$

10. $\quad 6\frac{2}{3}$
$\quad -\;\frac{3}{4}$

11. $\quad 1\frac{5}{8}$
$\quad -\;\frac{3}{4}$

12. $\quad 5\frac{2}{6}$
$\quad -3\frac{1}{2}$

13. $7\frac{1}{6} - 5\frac{2}{8} = $ _____

14. $2\frac{1}{6} - \frac{1}{5} = $ _____

15. $9\frac{2}{4} - 6\frac{11}{16} = $ _____

16. $4\frac{1}{3} - 1\frac{4}{5} = $ _____

Solve.

17. Carlos is $62\frac{3}{4}$ in. tall. Suzanne is $65\frac{1}{8}$ in. tall. How much taller is Suzanne than Carlos? _____

Practice

Student Book pp. 304–305

Solve.

1. Mrs. Richards wants to combine
   this juice into two one-gallon
   containers. Name two ways in
   which she could do it. _____

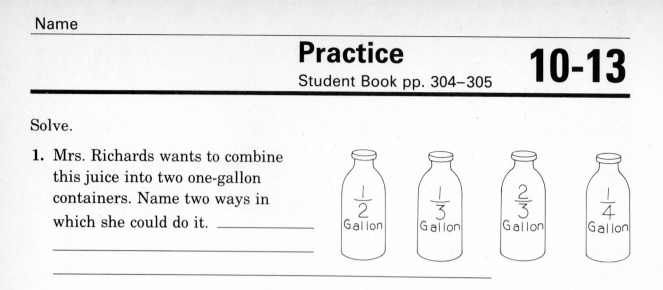

2. A square garden is 6 ft on each side. Show two ways to find
   the perimeter. _____

3. The perimeter of a square is $4 \times 6\frac{3}{4}$ in. Find the perimeter
   by using addition. _____

4. Arthur spent $12.69 at the sporting goods store. He gave the
   cashier a $20 bill. Name 3 different groups of bills and coins
   that the cashier could have given him as change. _____
   _____
   _____

5. What are two different ways to cut a $6\frac{1}{4}$ ft, a $3\frac{3}{4}$ ft and a
   $5\frac{1}{2}$ ft piece of board from two boards that are each 10 ft
   long? _____
   _____
   _____

6. What are two different ways to cut 2 boards each $3\frac{1}{2}$ ft long,
   and 3 boards each $1\frac{3}{4}$ ft long, from 2 boards that are each 7
   ft long? _____
   _____
   _____

Practice

Student Book pp. 314–315

11-1

Multiply $2 \times \frac{3}{4}$.

You can add.

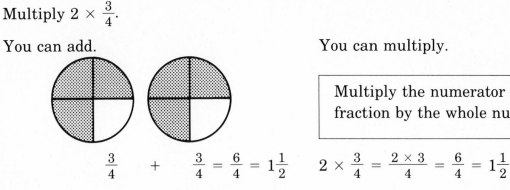

$$\frac{3}{4} \quad + \quad \frac{3}{4} = \frac{6}{4} = 1\frac{1}{2}$$

You can multiply.

Multiply the numerator of the fraction by the whole number.

$$2 \times \frac{3}{4} = \frac{2 \times 3}{4} = \frac{6}{4} = 1\frac{1}{2}$$

Multiply. Write the product in lowest terms.

1. $5 \times \frac{1}{3} =$ _____

2. $3 \times \frac{4}{5} =$ _____

3. $3 \times \frac{2}{7} =$ _____

4. $\frac{1}{9} \times 8 =$ _____

5. $3 \times \frac{2}{3} =$ _____

6. $\frac{1}{4} \times 2 =$ _____

7. $9 \times \frac{1}{6} =$ _____

8. $10 \times \frac{2}{5} =$ _____

9. $\frac{2}{3} \times 8 =$ _____

10. $11 \times \frac{1}{9} =$ _____

11. $4 \times \frac{2}{7} =$ _____

12. $\frac{3}{4} \times 8 =$ _____

13. $7 \times \frac{1}{3} =$ _____

14. $3 \times \frac{2}{9} =$ _____

15. $6 \times \frac{1}{5} =$ _____

16. $9 \times \frac{1}{2} =$ _____

17. $9 \times \frac{5}{6} =$ _____

18. $\frac{1}{2} \times 6 =$ _____

19. $\frac{3}{10} \times 5 =$ _____

20. $\frac{5}{6} \times 7 =$ _____

Solve. Write the answer in lowest terms.

21. Marc weighs 80 lb. Jane weighs $\frac{4}{5}$ as much. How much does Jane weigh? _____

22. Marcy's father put 2 qt of juice in the refrigerator. Marcy was very thirsty. During the day she drank $\frac{3}{4}$ of the juice. How much did Marcy drink? _____

Name _____

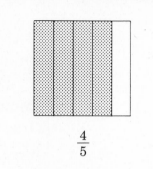

Here is a way to find $\frac{2}{3} \times \frac{4}{5}$.

$$\frac{4}{5}$$ 　　　　　　　$$\frac{2}{3} \text{ of } \frac{4}{5}$$

$$\frac{2}{3} \times \frac{4}{5} = \frac{2 \times 4}{3 \times 5} = \frac{8}{15}$$

Multiply. Write the product in lowest terms.

1. $\frac{3}{4} \times \frac{3}{5} =$ _____　　　2. $\frac{4}{9} \times \frac{3}{8} =$ _____

3. $\frac{3}{7} \times \frac{4}{5} =$ _____　　　4. $\frac{7}{8} \times \frac{3}{4} =$ _____

5. $\frac{2}{9} \times \frac{2}{5} =$ _____　　　6. $\frac{3}{5} \times \frac{2}{7} =$ _____

7. $\frac{5}{7} \times \frac{5}{6} =$ _____　　　8. $\frac{3}{8} \times \frac{6}{7} =$ _____

9. $\frac{3}{4} \times \frac{7}{10} =$ _____　　10. $\frac{3}{10} \times \frac{4}{5} =$ _____

11. $\frac{8}{9} \times \frac{2}{3} =$ _____　　12. $\frac{5}{6} \times \frac{3}{10} =$ _____

13. $\frac{4}{5} \times \frac{4}{5} =$ _____　　14. $\frac{5}{12} \times \frac{3}{4} =$ _____

15. $\frac{2}{9} \times \frac{5}{9} =$ _____　　16. $\frac{3}{7} \times \frac{3}{7} =$ _____

17. $\frac{3}{10} \times \frac{3}{10} =$ _____　18. $\frac{5}{6} \times \frac{5}{7} =$ _____

Solve. Write the answer in lowest terms.

19. Five eighths of the class is girls.
Two fifths of the girls are in the
band. What fraction of the girls are
in the band? _____

20. Four sevenths of all the concert
tickets were sold. One eighth of
those tickets were bought by
adults. What fraction of the tickets
sold were bought by adults? _____

A recipe calls for $1\frac{1}{2}$ c of flour. How many cups of flour would you need to triple the recipe?

You can estimate that $1\frac{1}{2}$ is between 1 and 2. The answer is between 3 and 6 because $3 \times 1 = 3$ and $3 \times 2 = 6$. The picture shows the exact answer.

$$1\frac{1}{2} + 1\frac{1}{2} + 1\frac{1}{2} = 4\frac{1}{2} \qquad\qquad 3 \times 1\frac{1}{2} = 4\frac{1}{2}$$

You need $4\frac{1}{2}$ c of flour to triple the recipe.

Complete. Write the answer in lowest terms.

1. $3 \times 5\frac{1}{4} = 5\frac{1}{4} + 5\frac{1}{4} + 5\frac{1}{4} = $ ____ **2.** $4 \times 3\frac{1}{8} = 3\frac{1}{8} + 3\frac{1}{8} + 3\frac{1}{8} + 3\frac{1}{8} = $ ____

3. $2 \times 5\frac{2}{3} = 5\frac{2}{3} + 5\frac{2}{3} = $ ____ **4.** $4 \times 2\frac{1}{5} = 2\frac{1}{5} + 2\frac{1}{5} + 2\frac{1}{5} + 2\frac{1}{5} = $ ____

5. $3 \times 4\frac{1}{3} = 4\frac{1}{3} + 4\frac{1}{3} + 4\frac{1}{3} = $ ____ **6.** $3 \times 3\frac{3}{5} = 3\frac{3}{5} + 3\frac{3}{5} + 3\frac{3}{5} = $ ____

7. $3 \times 2\frac{2}{5} = 2\frac{2}{5} + 2\frac{2}{5} + 2\frac{2}{5} = $ ____ **8.** $3 \times 4\frac{5}{6} = 4\frac{5}{6} + 4\frac{5}{6} + 4\frac{5}{6} = $ ____

Write two whole numbers between which the product lies.

9. $2 \times 3\frac{1}{5}$ _____ **10.** $3 \times 2\frac{1}{2}$ _____ **11.** $2 \times 4\frac{1}{3}$ _____

12. $5 \times 3\frac{1}{2}$ _____ **13.** $2\frac{1}{4} \times 5$ _____ **14.** $6\frac{1}{4} \times 10$ _____

Solve. Draw a picture or use addition to help.

15. Every week, the school cafeteria uses $5\frac{1}{2}$ bags of flour. How many bags of flour are used in 6 weeks? _____

16. The cafeteria uses $9\frac{1}{4}$ L of apple juice each day. How many liters are used in 5 days? _____

17. The cafeteria sells oranges every day after lunch. Each week, $6\frac{2}{3}$ crates of oranges are sold. How many crates of oranges are sold in 4 weeks? _____

Practice

11-4

To multiply mixed numbers, first write the mixed numbers as fractions and then multiply.

$$1\frac{2}{3} \times 2\frac{1}{2} = \frac{5}{3} \times \frac{5}{2} = \frac{25}{6} = 4\frac{1}{6}$$

$$2\frac{3}{4} \times 3 = \frac{11}{4} \times 3 = \frac{11 \times 3}{4} = \frac{33}{4} = 8\frac{1}{4}$$

Multiply. Write the product in lowest terms.

1. $\frac{3}{8} \times 4\frac{1}{2} =$ _____

2. $\frac{3}{8} \times 1\frac{3}{4} =$ _____

3. $1\frac{1}{9} \times 6 =$ _____

4. $2\frac{3}{7} \times 2 =$ _____

5. $3 \times 1\frac{3}{8} =$ _____

6. $2\frac{1}{5} \times 4 =$ _____

7. $1\frac{2}{3} \times 5 =$ _____

8. $6 \times 1\frac{3}{7} =$ _____

9. $2\frac{1}{9} \times 2 =$ _____

10. $\frac{6}{7} \times 2\frac{1}{2} =$ _____

11. $\frac{3}{5} \times 2\frac{3}{4} =$ _____

12. $3\frac{1}{3} \times 1\frac{1}{4} =$ _____

Estimate to decide if the answer is reasonable. Write *yes* or *no*.

13. $2\frac{1}{8} \times 1\frac{1}{2} = 3\frac{3}{16}$ _____

14. $5\frac{1}{3} \times 2\frac{5}{6} = 7\frac{5}{18}$ _____

15. $\frac{5}{7} \times 15\frac{2}{7} = 76\frac{3}{7}$ _____

16. $3\frac{2}{3} \times 5\frac{1}{8} = 18\frac{19}{24}$ _____

Solve.

17. A recipe called for liquids measuring 15 oz. If $9\frac{3}{4}$ oz of orange juice were needed and the rest was water, how many ounces of water were used? _____

18. A recipe for punch will serve 12 people. Margo makes $1\frac{1}{2}$ times the recipe. How many people will it serve? _____

19. Margo has a recipe that needs $1\frac{3}{4}$ c of raisins. If she doubles the recipe, how many cups of raisins will she need? _____

Practice

Student Book pp. 322–323 **11-5**

How many fourths are in three?

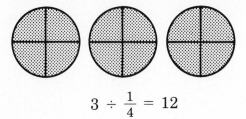

$$3 \div \frac{1}{4} = 12$$

How many fifths are in four?

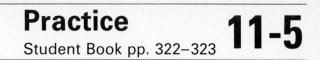

$$4 \div \frac{1}{5} = 20$$

Use the picture to divide.

1.

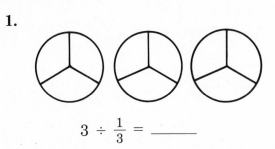

$$3 \div \frac{1}{3} = \underline{\qquad}$$

2.

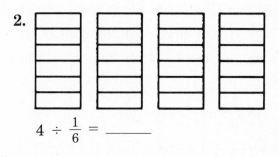

$$4 \div \frac{1}{6} = \underline{\qquad}$$

3.

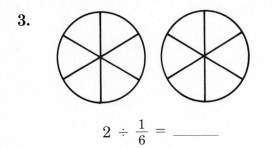

$$2 \div \frac{1}{6} = \underline{\qquad}$$

4.

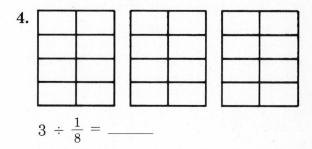

$$3 \div \frac{1}{8} = \underline{\qquad}$$

Divide. Draw a picture to help.

5. $5 \div \frac{1}{2} = \underline{\qquad}$

6. $6 \div \frac{1}{4} = \underline{\qquad}$

7. $3 \div \frac{1}{6} = \underline{\qquad}$

8. $4 \div \frac{1}{2} = \underline{\qquad}$

9. $4 \div \frac{1}{5} = \underline{\qquad}$

10. $2 \div \frac{1}{2} = \underline{\qquad}$

Solve. Draw a picture to help you.

11. Carl is making scarves for his
friends. He has 16 yd of material.
He needs $\frac{1}{2}$ yd for every scarf.
How many scarves can he make?

_____

Practice

Match the problem with the correct equation. Solve.

1. The sum of $6\frac{3}{5}$ and 4 is x. _____

2. The product of $6\frac{3}{5}$ and 4 is x. _____

3. The difference between $6\frac{3}{5}$ and 4 is x. _____

A. $6\frac{3}{5} \times 4 = x$

B. $6\frac{3}{5} + 4 = x$

C. $6\frac{3}{5} - 4 = x$

4. When Chen gets home from school, he studies for $2\frac{3}{4}$ h and practices the guitar for $\frac{1}{2}$ h. How much longer does he study than play the guitar? _____

5. Lucy rode her bicycle $2\frac{3}{4}$ km east and $\frac{1}{2}$ km north. How many kilometers did she ride in all? _____

6. Dominick needed $2\frac{3}{4}$ c of raisins for a granola recipe. If he makes $\frac{1}{2}$ of the recipe, how many raisins does he need? _____

A. $2\frac{3}{4} \times \frac{1}{2} = x$

B. $2\frac{3}{4} - \frac{1}{2} = x$

C. $2\frac{3}{4} + \frac{1}{2} = x$

Write a word problem using the equation.

7. $2\frac{1}{2} + 5 = x$

_____

_____

_____

_____

8. $2\frac{1}{4} + 3\frac{1}{4} + 1\frac{3}{4} = y$

_____

_____

_____

_____

Practice

Write each decimal as a fraction in lowest terms.

$$0.60 = 60 \text{ hundredths} = \frac{60}{100} = \frac{6}{10} = \frac{3}{5}$$
$$5.2 = 5 \text{ and } 2 \text{ tenths} = 5\frac{2}{10} = 5\frac{1}{5}$$

Write $\frac{3}{25}$ as a decimal.

$$\frac{3}{25} = \frac{12}{100} = 12 \text{ hundredths} = 0.12$$

Write as a fraction or mixed number in lowest terms.

1. 0.5 _____   **2.** 0.9 _____   **3.** 0.4 _____   **4.** 0.6 _____

5. 0.7 _____   **6.** 0.24 _____   **7.** 0.16 _____   **8.** 0.41 _____

9. 0.06 _____   **10.** 0.01 _____   **11.** 3.43 _____   **12.** 5.16 _____

13. 8.09 _____   **14.** 3.01 _____   **15.** 9.63 _____   **16.** 13.14 _____

17. 19.61 _____   **18.** 25.25 _____   **19.** 31.75 _____   **20.** 40.06 _____

21. 35.6 _____   **22.** 16.3 _____   **23.** 47.9 _____   **24.** 36.5 _____

Write as a decimal.

25. $\frac{8}{100}$ _____   **26.** $\frac{4}{50}$ _____   **27.** $\frac{2}{25}$ _____   **28.** $\frac{4}{20}$ _____

29. $\frac{1}{2}$ _____   **30.** $4\frac{3}{4}$ _____   **31.** $3\frac{1}{5}$ _____   **32.** $2\frac{2}{20}$ _____

33. $15\frac{7}{100}$ _____   **34.** $21\frac{1}{25}$ _____   **35.** $11\frac{3}{20}$ _____   **36.** $16\frac{1}{25}$ _____

37. $77\frac{2}{5}$ _____   **38.** $10\frac{3}{4}$ _____   **39.** $9\frac{4}{20}$ _____   **40.** $89\frac{1}{50}$ _____

41. $31\frac{4}{25}$ _____   **42.** $21\frac{1}{2}$ _____   **43.** $81\frac{3}{20}$ _____   **44.** $15\frac{3}{4}$ _____

45. $\frac{6}{25}$ _____   **46.** $1\frac{1}{5}$ _____   **47.** $2\frac{1}{2}$ _____   **48.** $\frac{4}{5}$ _____

Write as a decimal.

49. $\frac{3}{5} + \frac{1}{5}$ _____   **50.** $\frac{4}{5} + \frac{1}{4}$ _____   **51.** $5 \times 1\frac{3}{4}$ _____

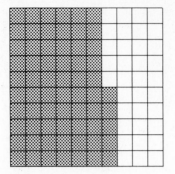

$\frac{65}{100}$ is shaded.

You can write any fraction that has a denominator of 100 as a percent. Percent means hundredths.

$\frac{65}{100}$ = 65 hundredths = 65%

You read 65% as 65 percent.

To write some fractions as percents, you first write an equivalent fraction with a denominator of 100.

$$\frac{3}{25} = \frac{12}{100} = 12\% \qquad\qquad \frac{10}{50} = \frac{20}{100} = 20\%$$

Write as a percent.

1. $\frac{35}{100}$ = _____   2. $\frac{6}{100}$ = _____   3. $\frac{65}{100}$ = _____   4. $\frac{13}{100}$ = _____

5. $\frac{52}{100}$ = _____   6. $\frac{1}{10}$ = _____   7. $\frac{10}{10}$ = _____   8. $\frac{3}{20}$ = _____

9. $\frac{10}{50}$ = _____   10. $\frac{9}{10}$ = _____   11. $\frac{8}{25}$ = _____   12. $\frac{35}{50}$ = _____

13. $\frac{7}{20}$ = _____   14. $\frac{11}{25}$ = _____   15. $\frac{13}{50}$ = _____   16. $\frac{20}{20}$ = _____

17. $\frac{4}{20}$ = _____   18. $\frac{12}{50}$ = _____   19. $\frac{17}{50}$ = _____   20. $\frac{19}{20}$ = _____

Write as a fraction in lowest terms.

21. 40% = _____   **22.** 20% = _____   **23.** 90% = _____   **24.** 60% = _____

25. 30% = _____   **26.** 55% = _____   **27.** 13% = _____   **28.** 89% = _____

29. 37% = _____   **30.** 62% = _____   **31.** 7% = _____   **32.** 65% = _____

33. 48% = _____   **34.** 4% = _____   **35.** 71% = _____   **36.** 33% = _____

37. 12% = _____   **38.** 8% = _____   **39.** 58% = _____   **40.** 85% = _____

Practice
Student Book pp. 330–331

> You can write a decimal as a percent.
>   0.86 = 86 hundredths = 86%
>   0.5 = 0.50 = 50 hundredths = 50%
>
> You can write a percent as a decimal.
>   47% = 47 hundredths = 0.47
>   60% = 60 hundredths = 0.60 = 0.6

Write as a percent.

1. 0.23 _____ **2.** 0.18 _____ **3.** 0.48 _____ **4.** 0.39 _____

5. 0.19 _____ **6.** 0.5 _____ **7.** 0.12 _____ **8.** 0.09 _____

9. 0.4 _____ **10.** 0.38 _____ **11.** 0.8 _____ **12.** 0.91 _____

13. 0.03 _____ **14.** 0.42 _____ **15.** 0.06 _____ **16.** 0.75 _____

17. 0.60 _____ **18.** 0.05 _____ **19.** 0.51 _____ **20.** 0.18 _____

Write as a decimal.

21. 42% _____ **22.** 18% _____ **23.** 30% _____ **24.** 49% _____

25. 29% _____ **26.** 90% _____ **27.** 53% _____ **28.** 6% _____

29. 14% _____ **30.** 3% _____ **31.** 37% _____ **32.** 100% _____

33. 4% _____ **34.** 25% _____ **35.** 7% _____ **36.** 18% _____

37. 2% _____ **38.** 8% _____ **39.** 75% _____ **40.** 20% _____

Draw a line to match.

41. $\frac{1}{2}$ 0.48

42. $\frac{12}{25}$ 0.8

43. 0.3   0.5

44. $\frac{4}{5}$ 4%

45. 0.03   0.25

46. 25%   30%

47. $\frac{2}{50}$ 3%

SALE TODAY ONLY!
Dresses.... 25% OFF
Suits....... 30% OFF

Practice
Student Book pp. 332–333

Complete.

	1.	2.	3.	4.	5.	6.	7.	8.
Fraction	$\frac{1}{2}$	$\frac{1}{4}$	$\frac{3}{4}$	$\frac{1}{5}$			$\frac{4}{5}$	
Decimal	0.5				0.4			0.1
Percent		25%				60%		10%

	9.	10.	11.	12.	13.	14.	15.	16.
Fraction	$\frac{3}{10}$	$\frac{7}{10}$			$\frac{13}{100}$			
Decimal			0.9			0.27		0.73
Percent				3%			49%	

Order the numbers from least to greatest.

17. $0.18, \frac{3}{20}, \frac{4}{8}$

18. $45\%, \frac{3}{4}, \frac{2}{5}$

_____

_____

19. $74\%, \frac{3}{5}, 0.62, \frac{4}{25}$

20. $\frac{3}{25}, 6\%, \frac{3}{4}, 0.48, \frac{6}{10}$

_____

_____

Complete.

21. Francine said, "Half the time I find it quicker to use my calculator." Frank said, "You mean _____ % of the time."

22. Judy said, "Three-quarters of these beans are lima beans." Jody said, "You mean _____ % of these beans are lima beans."

23. Cleo said, "My answer is $\frac{13}{100}$." Clyde said, "My calculator shows the answer as _____."

Practice

Student Book pp. 334–335

Use the pictures to write the ratios.

1. bats to racquets _____

2. footballs to soccer balls _____

3. racquets to bats _____

4. soccer balls to footballs _____

5. bats to racquets and bats _____

6. footballs to all balls _____

7. racquets and bats to racquets _____

8. all balls to soccer balls _____

Write the ratios for these statistics on volleyball.

9. 2 strikers to 6 players _____

10. 6 players to 12 players _____

11. 15 points to 4 points _____

12. 1 coach to 12 players _____

Write the ratios for these statistics on baseball.

13. 1 pitcher to 9 players _____

14. 3 fielders to 9 players _____

15. 5 hits to 8 hits _____

16. 2 runs to 5 hits _____

Estimate. Is the ratio closer to 0, $\frac{1}{2}$, or 1?

17. 2 strikes to 3 spares _____

18. 2 errors to 5 hits _____

19. 4 runs to 9 hits _____

20. 1 foul to 20 baskets _____

Solve.

21. The Blue Jays baseball team won 17 games and lost 14 games. What is the ratio of wins to losses? _____

22. During one game, Fernando Duma was at bat 3 times and had 2 hits. What is the ratio of hits to the number of times at bat? _____

Practice
Student Book pp. 336–337

Steven rode his bike 3 km in 15 minutes.
His rate of distance to time is $\frac{3}{15}$.

Diane rode her bike 12 km in 60 minutes.
Her rate of distance to time is $\frac{12}{60}$.

Steven and Diane rode their bikes at the same rate.

$$\frac{3}{15} = \frac{3 \times 4}{15 \times 4} = \frac{12}{60}$$

$\frac{3}{15}$ and $\frac{12}{60}$ are equivalent rates.

To find an equivalent rate, multiply or divide both parts of
the rate by the same number. Here are two examples.

$$\frac{3}{10} = \frac{3 \times 2}{10 \times 2} = \frac{6}{20} \qquad\qquad \frac{6}{8} = \frac{6 \div 2}{8 \div 2} = \frac{3}{4}$$

Complete to make the rates equivalent.

1. $\frac{1}{4} = \frac{}{12}$
2. $\frac{5}{9} = \frac{25}{}$
3. $\frac{4}{7} = \frac{28}{}$
4. $\frac{12}{18} = \frac{}{6}$

5. $\frac{30}{40} = \frac{6}{}$
6. $\frac{3}{10} = \frac{}{50}$
7. $\frac{6}{1} = \frac{18}{}$
8. $\frac{18}{4} = \frac{9}{}$

9. $\frac{15}{30} = \frac{3}{}$
10. $\frac{10}{25} = \frac{}{5}$
11. $\frac{25}{50} = \frac{1}{}$
12. $\frac{3}{7} = \frac{18}{}$

13. $\frac{2}{3} = \frac{}{30}$
14. $\frac{25}{100} = \frac{}{4}$
15. $\frac{2}{5} = \frac{}{20}$
16. $\frac{24}{27} = \frac{8}{}$

Are the rates equivalent? Write *yes* or *no*.

17. $\frac{4}{5} = \frac{12}{15}$ _____
18. $\frac{3}{4} = \frac{6}{24}$ _____
19. $\frac{3}{10} = \frac{25}{50}$ _____

20. $\frac{2}{5} = \frac{10}{25}$ _____
21. $\frac{10}{2} = \frac{5}{2}$ _____
22. $\frac{20}{4} = \frac{5}{1}$ _____

23. $\frac{10}{20} = \frac{1}{5}$ _____
24. $\frac{9}{12} = \frac{3}{4}$ _____
25. $\frac{2}{3} = \frac{6}{18}$ _____

Write an equivalent rate that is in lowest terms.

26. $\frac{8}{18} =$ _____
27. $\frac{2}{4} =$ _____
28. $\frac{6}{50} =$ _____
29. $\frac{4}{6} =$ _____

30. $\frac{9}{15} =$ _____
31. $\frac{3}{9} =$ _____
32. $\frac{75}{300} =$ _____
33. $\frac{21}{30} =$ _____

Practice
Student Book pp. 338–339

In this scale drawing $\frac{1}{4}$ in. represents 100 yd. Use the scale drawing to find the actual distance.

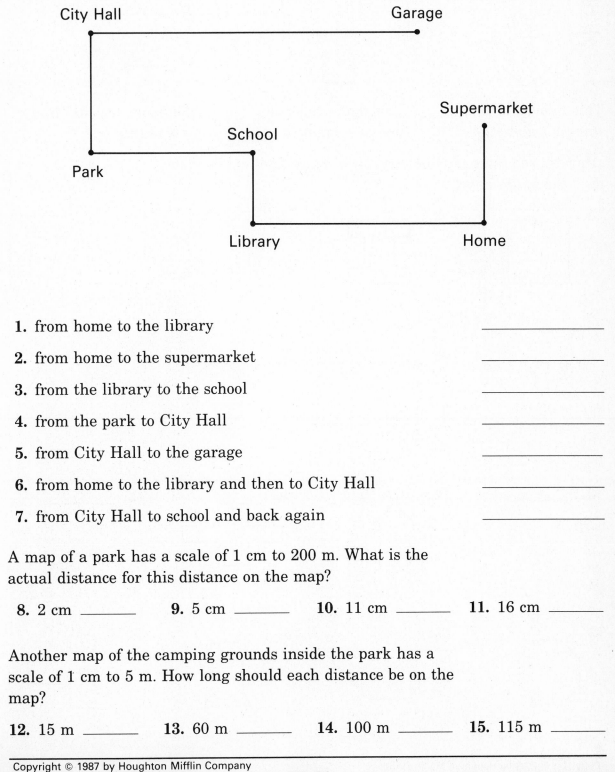

1. from home to the library _____

2. from home to the supermarket _____

3. from the library to the school _____

4. from the park to City Hall _____

5. from City Hall to the garage _____

6. from home to the library and then to City Hall _____

7. from City Hall to school and back again _____

A map of a park has a scale of 1 cm to 200 m. What is the actual distance for this distance on the map?

8. 2 cm _____   9. 5 cm _____   10. 11 cm _____   11. 16 cm _____

Another map of the camping grounds inside the park has a scale of 1 cm to 5 m. How long should each distance be on the map?

12. 15 m _____   13. 60 m _____   14. 100 m _____   15. 115 m _____

Practice
Student Book pp. 348–349
12-1

A figure has **line symmetry** if there is a line that separates the figure into two matching parts.

The rectangle has line symmetry. The line is called a **line of symmetry.**

This figure has no lines of symmetry.

This figure has one line of symmetry.

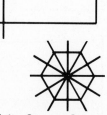

This figure has six lines of symmetry.

Draw all the lines of symmetry. How many lines of symmetry does the figure have?

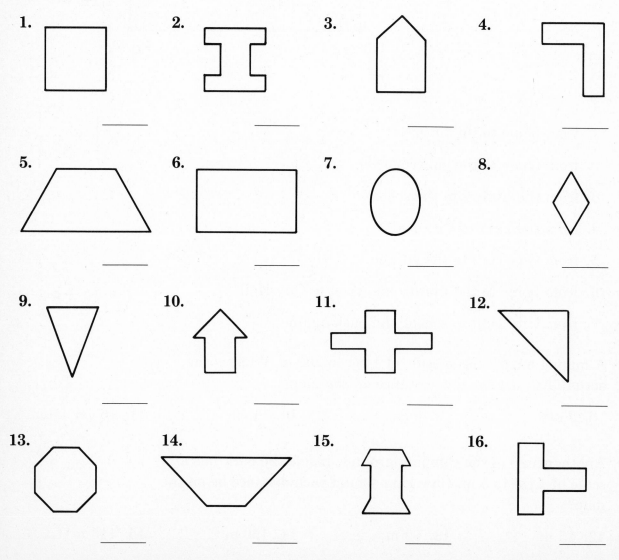

1.

2.

3.

4.

5.

6.

7.

8.

9.

10.

11.

12.

13.

14.

15.

16.

Practice

Student Book pp. 350–351 **12-2**

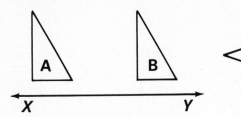
A fits on B if we *slide* it along line XY.

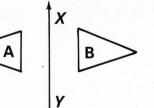
A fits on B if we *flip* it over line XY.

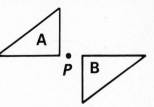
A fits on B if we *turn* it around point P.

Write S, F, or T to show whether we use a slide, a flip, or a turn to make A fit on B.

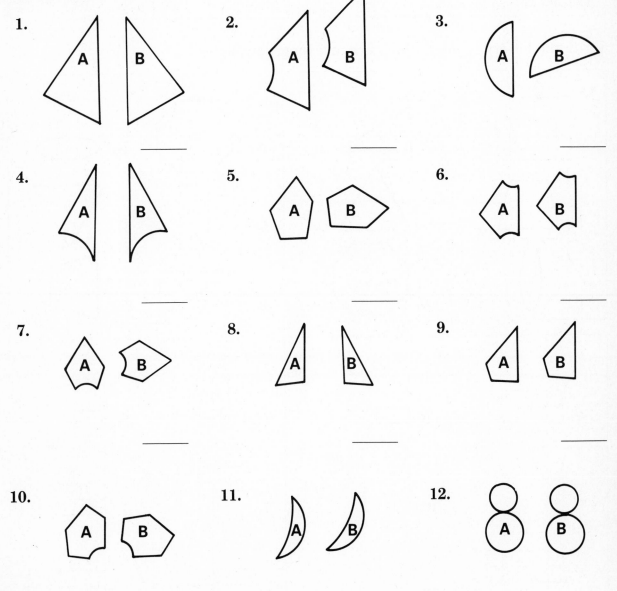

1. _____

2. _____

3. _____

4. _____

5. _____

6. _____

7. _____

8. _____

9. _____

10. _____

11. _____

12. _____

Practice
Student Book pp. 352–353 **12-3**

Figures are **congruent** if they are the same shape and size.

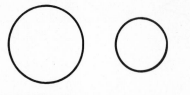

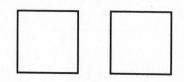

| The circles are *not* congruent. They are the same shape but they are not the same size. | The squares are *congruent*. They are the same shape and the same size. |

Write the letter to match the figure to a congruent figure.

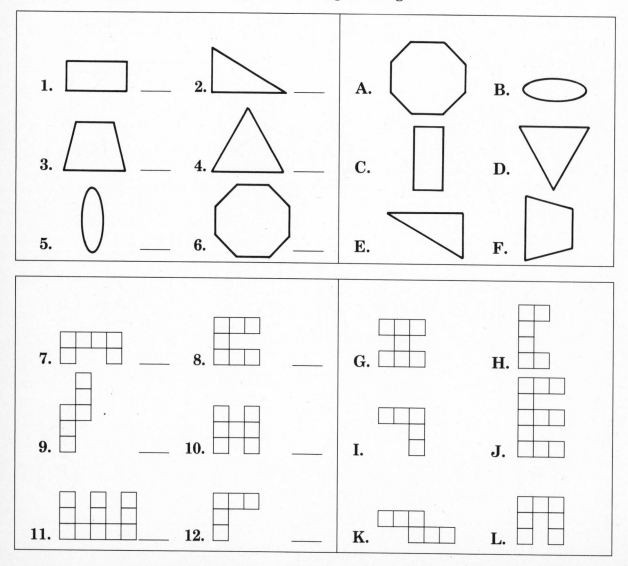

1. ____ 2. ____ A. B.

3. ____ 4. ____ C. D.

5. ____ 6. ____ E. F.

7. ____ 8. ____ G. H.

9. ____ 10. ____ I. J.

11. ____ 12. ____ K. L.

Figures that are the same shape but not necessarily the same
size are **similar**.

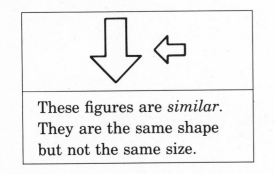

These figures are *similar*.
They are the same shape
but not the same size.

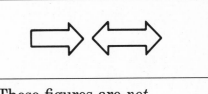

These figures are *not
similar*. They have
different shapes.

Circle the figure that is similar.

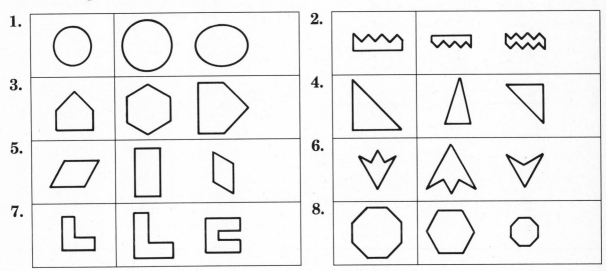

1.

2.

3.

4.

5.

6.

7.

8.

Solve.

9. Draw a rectangle 2 cm by 4 cm. Multiply the length of each
   side by 2. Draw a similar rectangle using these measures.

10. The perimeter of the second rectangle is how many times
    greater than the perimeter of the first rectangle? _____

Practice
Student Book pp. 356–357
12-5

Draw the next figure or number in the sequence.

1. ⇨ ⇩ ⇦ ⇧ ⇨ ____   2. ◇ ◇ ◇ ◇ ◇ ____

3. ◯ ⊖ ⊕ ☐ ⊟ ____   4. ⊕ ⊕ ⊕ ⊕ ⊕ ____

5. ✳ ⊕ ✳ ⊕ ✳ ____   6. ◁ ▷ ▽ ◇ ◁ ____

7. ◁ ▷ ▷ ◁ ◁ ____   8. ⊠ ⊠ ⊠ ✕ ✕ ⊠ ____

9. 1 9 2 8 3 7 _____   10. 2 1 4 3 6 5 _____

Start at the arrow. Follow the path shown in the example.
Continue the pattern to complete each box.

Example

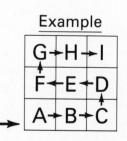

11. 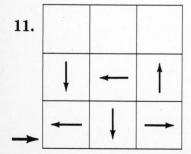   12. 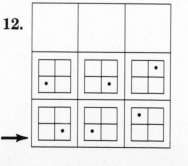   13.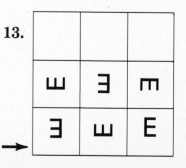

Practice
Student Book pp. 358–359

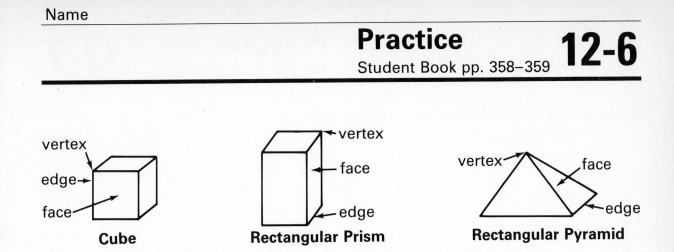

vertex · edge · face

Cube

vertex · face · edge

Rectangular Prism

vertex · face · edge

Rectangular Pyramid

The *faces* of the above figures are polygons. The faces meet in *edges* and the edges meet in *vertexes*.

Complete the chart.

	Figure	Name of figure	Number of faces	Number of edges	Number of vertexes
1.		Cube	____ square faces		
2.		Rectangular Prism	____ rectangular faces		
3.		Rectangular Pyramid	____ triangular faces ____ rectangular face		

Write cube, rectangular prism, or rectangular pyramid, to best describe the figure.

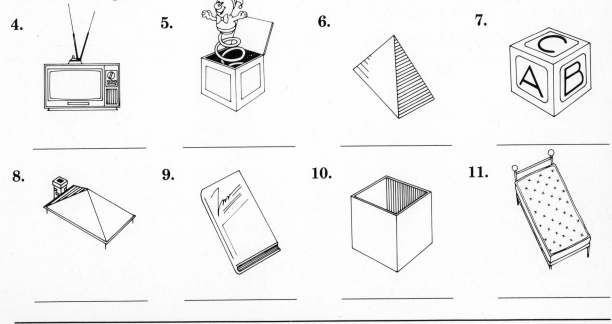

4.

5.

6.

7.

8.

9.

10.

11.

Practice

Student Book pp. 360–361

Complete the chart.

Figure	Name of Figure	Number of Faces	Number of Vertexes
1. cylinder (face, face)	cylinder	____ flat circular faces	____
2. cone (vertex, face)	cone	____ flat circular face	____
3. sphere	sphere	____ flat faces	____

Write *cylinder, cone,* or *sphere* to best name the figure.

4. _____   5. _____   6. _____   7. _____

8. _____   9. _____   10. _____   11. _____

12. _____   13. _____   14. _____   15. _____

Write *cylinder, cone,* or *sphere.* Use the drawings below that show the way the figure looks from the top and the side.

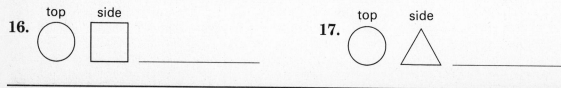

16. top (circle) side (square) _____   17. top (circle) side (triangle) _____

Practice
Student Book pp. 362–363 **12-8**

The **volume** of a figure is the number of cubic units it contains.

A **cubic centimeter** is a common unit for measuring volume.

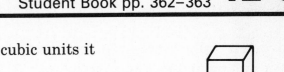

one cubic centimeter
(1 cm³)

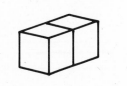

The volume of this figure is 11 cm³.

What is the volume of the figure?

1.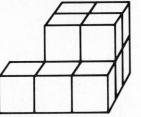

2.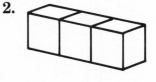

3.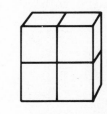

_____ _____ _____

4.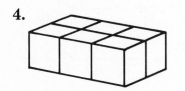

5.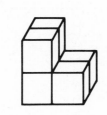

6.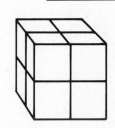

_____ _____ _____

7.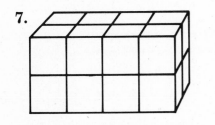

8.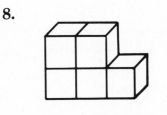

9.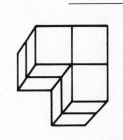

_____ _____ _____

10.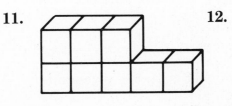

11.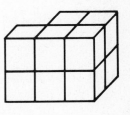

12.

_____ _____ _____

Name _____

The divers found a treasure chest that is 0.7 m long, 0.3 m wide, and 0.5 m high. To find the **volume** of the box, multiply the length by the width by the height.

$$V = l \times w \times h$$
$$V = 0.7 \times 0.3 \times 0.5$$
$$V = 0.105 \text{ m}^3$$

The volume of the box is 0.105 m^3.

What is the volume?

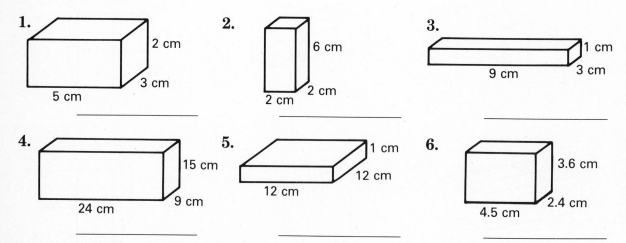

1. 2 cm 3 cm 5 cm

_____

2. 6 cm 2 cm 2 cm

_____

3. 1 cm 3 cm 9 cm

_____

4. 15 cm 9 cm 24 cm

_____

5. 1 cm 12 cm 12 cm

_____

6. 3.6 cm 2.4 cm 4.5 cm

_____

What is the volume of a rectangular prism with the given length, width, and height?

7. $l = 8$ cm
$w = 4$ cm
$h = 2$ cm
$V = $ _____

8. $l = 5$ m
$w = 2$ m
$h = 3$ m
$V = $ _____

9. $l = 20$ cm
$w = 15$ cm
$h = 16$ cm
$V = $ _____

10. $l = 5$ m
$w = 3$ m
$h = 2.4$ m
$V = $ _____

11. $l = 8$ cm
$w = 3.4$ cm
$h = 6.2$ cm
$V = $ _____

12. $l = 2.3$ m
$w = 4.1$ m
$h = 3.4$m
$V = $ _____

What is the volume of a cube with the given side?

13. $s = 15$ m
$V = $ _____

14. $s = 30$ cm
$V = $ _____

15. $s = 6.8$ m
$V = $ _____

Practice

Student Book pp. 366–367

Draw a picture for each problem. Solve.

1. A swimming pool is 40 ft long, 20 ft wide, and 8 ft deep. What is the volume of the pool? _____

2. Next to the swimming pool, there is a rectangular area that is roped off for spectators. The area is 36 ft long and 24 ft wide. What is the perimeter of the area? _____

3. There is a rectangular flower garden at one end of the pool that is 12 ft long and 8 ft wide. What is the area of the flower garden? _____

Make up a problem in which you use each of the following. Draw a picture to go along with each problem.

4. perimeter of a square _____

_____

_____

_____

5. volume of a cube _____

_____

_____

_____

6. area of a rectangle _____

_____

_____

_____

Name _____

The owner of Sam's Shoe Store listed the numbers of pairs of shoes sold in a week. Numbers that give information are called *data*.

Day	Mon.	Tues.	Wed.	Thurs.	Fri.	Sat.	Sun.
Pairs of Shoes Sold	24	18	21	26	29	35	29

The difference between the least and greatest numbers is called the *range*.

$$35 - 18 = 17$$

The range for the numbers of pairs of shoes sold is 17.

The middle number when the numbers are put in order is called the *median*.

18, 21, 24, (26), 29, 29, 35

The median number of pairs of shoes sold is 26.

The number that appears most often in the data is the *mode*. The number 29 occurs twice. The mode is 29.

Complete the chart.

	Data	Range	Median	Mode
1.	2, 5, 10, 3, 5			
2.	6, 25, 4, 9, 9, 8, 2			
3.	38, 42, 42, 15, 41, 34, 35			
4.	200, 108, 150, 174, 150			
5.	$34, $59, $23, $59, $75			
6.	17.3 m, 2.6 m, 4.9 m, 3.7 m, 3.7 m			
7.	46%, 28%, 35%, 16%, 18%, 18%, 67%			
8.	2.5 L, 3.4 L, 6.7 L, 7.4 L, 2.5 L			
9.	19%, 21%, 43%, 35%, 21%, 81%, 79%			
10.	143, 281, 29, 29, 133			

Jan made a list of the number of children absent from school during one week. Her list is below.

Day	Mon.	Tues.	Wed.	Thurs.	Fri.
Number of Children Absent	43	35	21	25	36

Follow the steps below to find the average number of children absent each day.

Another name for average is mean.

Add the numbers.

43
35
21
25
+36
___
160

Divide the sum by the number of addends.

$$\begin{array}{r} 32 \\ 5\overline{)160} \\ -15 \\ \hline 10 \\ -10 \\ \hline 0 \end{array}$$

The mean number of children absent each day is 32.

What is the mean?

1. 4, 6, 8 _____

2. 40, 60, 30, 50 _____

3. 43, 94, 63, 42, 68 _____

4. 223, 336, 468, 953 _____

5. 4.3, 2.6, 4.2 _____

6. 6.4, 4.1, 2.3, 4.4 _____

7. 22.3, 34.3, 49.8, 29.2 _____

8. 43.4, 30.2, 45.4, 34.6 _____

9. 8 cm, 12 cm, 10 cm _____

10. 4 kg, 3 kg, 8 kg, 5 kg _____

11. 42%, 65%, 97%, 84% _____

12. 38%, 64%, 50%, 24% _____

13. $3.75, $4.25, $5.50, $2.50 _____

14. $2.39, $3.43, $5.15, $6.43 _____

Solve.

15. Jan's math grades were 94, 95, 87, 93, 81. What is Jan's average math score? _____

16. Jan and 3 of her classmates were measured during the first week of school. Their heights were 148 cm, 156 cm, 145 cm, and 151 cm. What was their average height? _____

Practice
Student Book pp. 380–381
13-3

Mary and John made a double bar graph to compare the amount of time they spent practicing the piano.

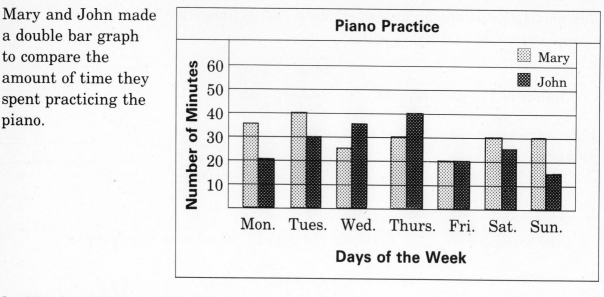

Piano Practice

On Monday, Mary practiced for 35 min and John practiced for 20 min.

Use the double bar graph above to answer the questions.

For how long did Mary practice each day?

1. Monday _____   2. Wednesday _____   3. Thursday _____
4. Tuesday _____   5. Saturday _____   6. Friday _____

For how long did John practice each day?

7. Monday _____   8. Wednesday _____   9. Thursday _____
10. Tuesday _____   11. Saturday _____   12. Friday _____

Solve.

13. On which day did John and Mary practice the same amount of time? _____

14. On which days did John practice longer than Mary? _____

15. On Monday, who practiced longer? _____ How much longer? _____

16. What was the total number of minutes Mary practiced? _____

17. What was the mean number of minutes Mary practiced? _____

Name _____

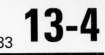

Reggie made a pictograph to show the number of cars that passed his school at different times of the day.

Number of Cars

8 A.M. - 9 A.M.	🚗 🚗 🚗 🚗 🚗 🚗 🚗
9 A.M. - 10 A.M.	🚗 🚗 🚗 🚗 🚗 🚗 🚗 🚗
10 A.M. - 11 A.M.	🚗 🚗 🚗 🚗 ▯
12 noon - 1 P.M.	🚗 🚗 🚗 🚗 🚗 ▯
1 P.M. - 2 P.M.	🚗 🚗 🚗 🚗 🚗 🚗 ▯

Each 🚗 means 10 cars.
Each ▯ means 5 cars.

Use the pictograph to answer these questions.

1. How many cars passed between 8 A.M. and 9 A.M.? _____

2. How many cars passed between 1 P.M. and 2 P.M.? _____

3. How many cars passed between noon and 2 P.M.? _____

4. Between 11 A.M. and noon, 25 cars passed.
   How many cars passed between 8 A.M. and noon? _____

5. For the times shown on the table, when did the most cars pass the school? _____

6. For the times shown on the table, when did the fewest cars pass the school? _____

7. How many more cars passed between 8 A.M. and 10 A.M. than between 10 A.M. and 11 A.M.? _____

8. A total of 175 cars passed between 1 P.M. and 4 P.M. How many more cars passed from 8 A.M. to 11 A.M. than from 1 P.M. to 4 P.M.? _____

Practice
Student Book pp. 384–385 **13-5**

Fred kept track of his earnings from his newspaper route for 6 weeks. Here is a line graph showing how much money he earned each week.

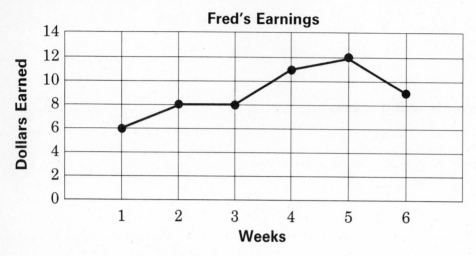

Fred earned $6 during week 1.

Use the line graph to answer.

How much money did Fred earn during the given week?

1. Week 3 _____   2. Week 4 _____   3. Week 6 _____

4. During which week did Fred earn the most money? _____
   How much did he earn? _____

5. During which week did Fred earn the least amount of money? _____ How much did he earn? _____

6. Did Fred earn more money during week 5 or 6? _____
   How much more? _____

7. During which weeks did Fred earn the same amount of money? _____

8. Between which 2 weeks did Fred's earnings increase the most? _____
   How much did they increase? _____

9. How much money did Fred earn in the 6 weeks? _____

10. What was the mean amount of money that Fred earned each week? _____

Practice

This circle graph shows how Lisa spends her allowance each week.

    20% on entertainment
    15% on savings
    10% on clothing
  + 55% on lunch
    100%

The sum of the percents is 100%, Lisa's entire allowance.

Allowance

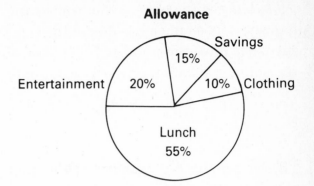

Look at the circle graph at the right. Use the graph to answer the questions.

Sports Played by Some Fifth Graders

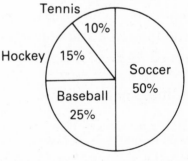

1. What percent of the students play soccer?

    _____

2. What percent of the students play baseball?

    _____

3. What percent of the students play tennis?

    _____

4. What is the total percent of students that play soccer, tennis, hockey, and baseball? _____

5. What is the difference between the percent of students that play soccer and the percent of students that play hockey? _____

Look at the circle graph at the right. Solve.

Pets Owned by Students in Mrs. Brown's Class

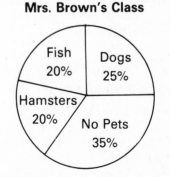

6. What percent of the students own dogs?

    _____

7. What percent of the students own hamsters?

    _____

8. Does a larger percent of the students own dogs or fish? _____

9. Which two pets are each owned by the same percent of the students?

    _____

10. If there are 40 students in Mrs. Brown's class, how many students own dogs? _____

Probability is the chance that something will happen. The spinner has 8 equal parts. Three of the parts have the number 7. The probability of the spinner stopping on a 7 is 3 out of 8.

You can write a probability as a fraction.
3 out of 8 = $\frac{3}{8}$

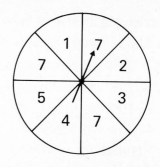

The probability of the spinner stopping on 1 is $\frac{1}{8}$. It is less likely that the spinner will stop at 1 than at 7.

There is no 6 on the spinner. The probability of the spinner stopping at 6 is $\frac{0}{8}$, or 0.

Suppose you turn these cards face down on a desk and you pick one card without looking. What is the probability of choosing the given letter? Write the probability as a fraction in lowest terms.

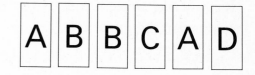

1. A _____ **2.** B _____ **3.** C _____

4. D _____

Suppose you spin the spinner. What is the probability of the spinner stopping on each number? Write the probability as a fraction in lowest terms.

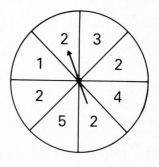

5. 2 _____ **6.** 1 _____ **7.** 3 _____

8. 4 _____ **9.** 5 _____ **10.** 6 _____

11. an even number _____

12. an odd number _____

Suppose there are 5 marbles in a container. Two are green, two are red, and one is blue. What is the probability of choosing the given color?

13. red _____ **14.** blue _____ **15.** green _____ **16.** yellow _____

17. Which two colors have an equal chance of being chosen? _____

If you turn these cards face down on your desk and choose a card without looking, what is the probability of choosing an R or an S?

| R | T | R | S | R | T | T | R |

The probability of choosing an R is $\frac{4}{8}$.
The probability of choosing an S is $\frac{1}{8}$.
The probability of choosing an R or an S is $\frac{4}{8} + \frac{1}{8}$, or $\frac{5}{8}$.

Amy has 6 blue socks, 8 brown socks, 6 black socks, and 10 white socks in a drawer. If she closes her eyes and picks one sock, what is the probability that she will choose a sock of one of the given colors?

1. blue or white _____
2. blue or brown _____
3. blue or black _____
4. brown or white _____
5. brown or black _____
6. black or white _____

Suppose you spin the spinner at the right. What is the probability of it stopping on one of the given numbers?

7. 1 or 2 _____
8. 1 or 3 _____
9. 1 or 4 _____
10. 2 or 5 _____
11. 3 or 4 _____
12. 1 or an even number _____

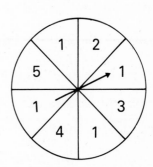

Suppose you choose a letter, without looking, from the word CALCULATOR. What is the probability of choosing the following?

13. a vowel _____
14. a consonant _____
15. a C or an A _____
16. a C or an R _____
17. an O or a U _____
18. an L or a vowel _____

Practice

There are 1000 students at Hoover School. Of these students a sample of 200 were asked to name their favorite sport. The answers were recorded on a tally chart as follows.

Favorite Sport of Students at Hoover School

Softball	ЖЖ ЖЖ ЖЖ ЖЖ ЖЖ ЖЖ ЖЖ ЖЖ ЖЖ ЖЖ ЖЖ ЖЖ ЖЖ
Football	ЖЖ ЖЖ ЖЖ ЖЖ ЖЖ ЖЖ ЖЖ ЖЖ ЖЖ ЖЖ ЖЖ ЖЖ
Basketball	ЖЖ ЖЖ ЖЖ ЖЖ ЖЖ ЖЖ ЖЖ ЖЖ ЖЖ ЖЖ
Track and Field	ЖЖ ЖЖ ЖЖ ЖЖ ЖЖ

Of the 200 students sampled, 65 students chose softball as their favorite sport.

To predict how many of the 1000 students at Hoover School would choose softball as their favorite sport, multiply $\frac{65}{100}$ or $\frac{13}{40}$ by 1000.

$$\frac{13}{40} \times 1000 = 325 \text{ students}$$

325 students probably will choose softball.

Use the chart to answer the questions below.

1. How many of the 200 students chose basketball? _____

2. How many of the 200 students chose football? _____

3. How many of the 200 students chose track and field? _____

Use the information in the chart to predict the answers to the questions.

4. What fraction of the sample chose football? _____

5. About how many of the 1000 students at Hoover School would choose football? _____

6. What fraction of the sample chose basketball? _____

7. About how many of the 1000 students at Hoover School would choose basketball? _____

8. What fraction of the sample chose track and field? _____

9. About how many of the 1000 students at Hoover School would choose track and field? _____